Communicating
with BOLD
Assurance

Bert Decker

LifeWay Press
Nashville, Tennessee

ISBN 0-6330-0333-6

Dewey Decimal Classification Number: 302.2
Subject Heading: COMMUNICATION \ PUBLIC SPEAKING \ TEACHING

This book is the text for course LS-0049 (Discipleship Training)
in the Christian Growth Study Plan.

Unless otherwise noted, Scripture quotations are from the Holy Bible,
New International Version, copyright © 1973, 1978, 1984 by International Bible Society.

Scripture quotations identified NKJV are from the *New King James Version.*
Copyright © 1979, 1980, 1982, Thomas Nelson, Inc., Publishers.

Scripture quotations identified KJV are from the *King James Version.*

LifeWay Christian Resources vision statement:
*As God works through us, we will help people and churches
know Jesus Christ and seek His kingdom by providing biblical solutions
that spiritually transform individuals and cultures.*

Printed in the United States of America

LifeWay Press
127 Ninth Avenue, North
Nashville, Tennessee 37234-0150

Contents

About the Author

Bert Decker, is a communication expert who met the Master Communicator, Jesus Christ, and his life was radically changed. Bert has been on NBC's "TODAY Show" many times as their communications expert, commenting on the presidential debates of 1992 and 1996. He is the author of the best-selling book, *You've Got to Be Believed to Be Heard.* Bert has been featured in *The Wall Street Journal* and on ABC's "20/20," as well as in full page articles in *Business Week,* the *New York Times,* and *Success* Magazine.

Bert is Chairman and Founder of Decker Communications, Inc., a consulting company of 100 people with offices in San Francisco, New York, Chicago, Los Angeles, Washington, and Boston. Decker Communications is now a subsidiary of Provant, Inc., the world's largest performance improvement training company.

In addition to his business interests, Bert founded and is Chairman of Bold Assurance Ministries, a non-profit corporation that increases speaking confidence and skills with God-given principles. As a Christian, Bert believes that Christians have the most important message, the gospel of our Lord Jesus Christ. Bert's passion is training Christians to be effective communicators so that they can share their stories with those with no hope. Bold Assurance Ministries provides programs and products, speeches, and seminars to the Christian community.

Bert was a main platform speaker at the Million Dollar Round Table and the Willow Creek Leadership Summit. He personally coaches CEO's such as Charles Schwab and major sports figures like Olympic Gold Medal winner Bonnie Blair and All Pro football star Brent Jones. He graduated from Yale University with a psychology degree, and serves on the Board of Directors of Provant, Connecting Business and the Marketplace to Christ (CBMC), and Westmont College. Bert lives in San Francisco with his wife Dru Scott.

Foreword

God made us to communicate. He did not create us to live or talk passively, but to live life fully. Moses didn't want to communicate, and God said, *"Now go; I will help you speak and will teach you what to say"* (Ex. 4:12). He said something similar to others in the Bible—Joshua, Gideon, David, Peter, and even Paul, because every one of them did not want to speak—at first.

Communicating with Bold Assurance builds speaking confidence with God-given principles. It is a powerful and proven resource that has helped participants have the motivation to communicate, the skills to do it more effectively with a "Forward Lean," and to find new opportunities to express their words and God's Word. I'm glad you are in this program, and I'm excited about leading it. The principles here have changed my life, and I think they can change yours as well.

What you are about to experience is a communications program that is a confluence of spiritual principles with practical tools. The spiritual principles from the Bible have been proven over the last 2,000 years. The practical tools of speaking excellence have been proven over the last 20 years, with over 150,000 confident graduates from the nationally known Decker Effective Communicating Program. From top executives to terrified beginners, all have gained effectiveness, confidence, and skill through using the principles that my company teaches in the business world. But this is the first time that both the spiritual and the practical have come together in one program. It is a powerful combination.

To those of you who are already experienced communicators—pastors, teachers, lay leaders—you will learn dozens of behavioral skills, how to organize your ideas very quickly and how to escape the necessity of reading speeches and sermons. You will learn new insights in what God says about your teaching and leading. For those less experienced, and maybe even terrified of speaking, you will gain the skills and confidence to speak out in situations that you never thought you'd dare. And of course you will learn all the skills and spiritual principles as well.

Communicating with Bold Assurance has changed the way people communicate Christ, and enhanced the effectiveness of their speaking in all areas of their lives. I pray that it does the same for you.

May God bless you fully,

Introduction

Welcome to *Communicating with Bold Assurance*. The purpose of this course is to help Christians become better communicators so they can effectively share Jesus with others. As Christians, we have the most important message—the gospel of Jesus Christ. We communicate the good news of Jesus and the difference He has made in our lives primarily through speaking. *Consequently, faith comes from hearing the message, and the message is heard through the word of Christ* (Rom. 10:17). The goal of author Bert Decker is to train Christians to be excellent communicators so that when they share the story of their changed lives their communication skills positively impact their message and do not create a hindrance to the gospel.

Communication is a broad term so it is important to narrow the scope of this topic. The focus of this course is verbal communication. The audience you speak to can be one person, a small group, or an auditorium filled with people. The communication skills that are covered in this book can be applied to any listener or group of people.

Bert Decker is a communications expert. He will demonstrate how the spoken word is different from the written word. He will help you to understand the importance to reaching the heart of your listeners. Verbal communication relates to seeing, hearing, and feeling. You will learn Nine Behavioral Skills that have a positive impact on how your message is received by the listener. When a speaker is unaware of these skills, it can have a negative influence on the message that is communicated.

Bert developed the Decker Grid System as a tool to help speakers develop their presentation. He has trained thousands of people through Decker Communications, Inc., and through Bold Assurance Ministries. In the Workbook and video, Bert will guide you step-by-step as you learn to use the Decker Grid System. You will be amazed by the simplicity and effectiveness of this method of preparation.

The *Communicating with Bold Assurance* Workbook is a part of a family of resources to help you as a communicator. The *Communicating with Bold Assurance Kit* is a video driven course. Bert Decker presents the essence of *Communicating with Bold Assurance* to a live audience. The *Communicating with Bold Assurance Leader's Guide* provides instructions for leading a small group through this study. The ideal way to receive the greatest benefit from this study is to participate in a small-group experience. The course is a highly interactive, eight-session format. Each week you meet with a small group and view the video training. Then there is a small-group follow-up session where participants put into practice the principles taught by Bert on video. The weekly sessions are 1 hour 30 minutes in duration. The Workbook provides reinforcement to the principles given in the video and small-group experience. There are also four audio tapes (eight sessions) in the Kit that reinforce the principles of *Communicating with Bold Assurance*. By following this format you receive the full benefit of the study.

Here are some Action Steps to take. Get involved with a small group of people and participate in *Communicating with Bold Assurance*. Take advantage of the total package of training given in the Kit. Take the initiative to lead this study in your church or with a group in your community.

The Benefits of being involved in this small-group experience are many:
• You will become a more effective communicator.
• You will learn how to share your faith story with those who do not know Jesus Christ.
• You will enjoy the small-group experience.
• You will receive valuable feedback from your peers in this study.

Communicating with Bold Assurance will benefit anyone who participates in this study. If you do not do public speaking and the thought of giving a presentation terrifies you, you will discover helps for your interpersonal, one-to-one communications. If you teach a Sunday School class or facilitate small-group studies, this course will help you to be more effective in presenting your message. If you give presentations in your workplace or are a teacher, you will discover skills that will enhance your communication. If you have a desire to share your faith with others, this course will help you. If you are an experienced speaker you will find that this course is filled with ideas that will help you to evaluate your presentations and your communication behavioral skills.

Communicating with Bold Assurance will transform your everyday life. The speaking methodology is rated as the best in the country, but the power of the study is centered on God's promises.

We would like to hear from you!

For information or questions about *Communicating with Bold Assurance* contact the Discipleship & Family Leadership Department—
   Telephone: 615-251-2833
   Email: boldassurance@lifeway.com
   LifeWay website: www.lifeway.com
   Write to us at: LifeWay Christian Resources
                   127 Ninth Avenue North
                   Nashville, Tennessee 37234

To find out more about Bold Assurance Ministries visit the website at www.boldassurance.com

*"Now go; I will help you speak and
will teach you what to say."*
—Exodus 4:12

*For the Lord will be
your confidence.*
—Proverbs 3:26

*For God did not give us a spirit of
timidity, but a spirit of power,
of love and of self-discipline.*
—2 Timonthy 1:7

The righteous are as bold as a lion.
—Proverbs 28:1

Session 1:

Communicating with Confidence

God made us to _Communicate_.

1. Nervous Energy

   Greatest Fears

   Speaking _41_ %

   Death _19_ %

We need to have a _forward lean_ about our communications.

The Four Stages of Speaking

   1. Nonspeaker: Emotion is _terror_.   12%

      Behavior tends toward avoidance.

   2. Occasional: Emotion is _fear_.   57%

      Behavior tends toward reluctance.

   3. Willing: Emotion is _tension_.   25%

      Behavior tends toward willingness.

   4. Leader: Emotion is _stimulation_.   6%

      Behavior tends toward eagerness.

- _95_ % of the time we try something, we will succeed!

Proverbs 3:26: _For the Lord will be your_ _confidence_.

2. What Really Counts

What impacts believability? *by Albert Varabian*
Silent Messages

Verbal ___7___ % 20

Vocal ___38___ % 20

Visual ___55___ % 60

People buy on ___emotion___ and justify with fact.

The Concept of "First Brain"

The First Brain is our ___emotional___ brain, and serves as a conduit for sending stimulus and input to the Thinking Brain—which is our analytical brain.

All five senses are connected to the ___first___ ___brain___.

We want our ideas to go directly to our conscious and rational Thinking Brain, but they have to pass through the unconscious ___first___ ___brain___ first.

People buy on emotion and justify with ___fact___.

3. Enthusiasm

What is the age of the most effective communicator? ___2 year olds___

Communicating is a ___contact___ ___sport___.

1. Think of your first speaking experience. What has changed since then in your feeling and ability to speak?

2. Who was your favorite teacher? What does that say for effective communicating? *passion came through in their speaking*

3. In what Stage of Speaking are you? Where do you think you can be, and what would it take to get there? *Willing, practice, focus, passion, reason*

4. When you last gave a speech, what is the comparative percentage of time you spent preparing your content versus preparing your voice and visual impact? Why do you think many people read speeches? Do you think reading speeches is a crutch?

Communicating
with Confidence

For God did not give us a spirit of timidity, but a spirit of power, of love and of self-discipline.

2 Timothy 1:7

Find a time and place where you will be totally alone. Read aloud 2 Timothy 1:7. Now, claim the promise in this verse. Pray out loud asking God to give you power, love, and self-discipline. Ask Him to help you to learn and to apply the methods from this course. Review what you learned from the video by reviewing pages 9-10 in this Workbook. In the space below, write one action that you will try to use this week from what you learned from the video.

focus on my visual message, speak w/ confidence on Sundial - sell it. Sell myself.

DAY 1

God Made Us to Communicate

We are born with the God-given ability to communicate. If we are to reach our capacity and become effective communicators, it takes awareness and training. Just saying the words is not enough—we must connect on a personal level with our audience, whether it is one person or a large group. In speaking, confidence in God's ability to use us for His purpose is critical to our success, and increased confidence can be ours when we learn to rely on God to guide and work through us.

God made us to communicate, and He made us able to communicate in a way that will affect people and will reach people for God's purposes. We have an example—Jesus Christ. When He said, *"For I did not speak of my own accord, but the Father who sent me commanded me what to say, and how to say it"* (John 12:49), He was showing us how we should communicate. God gives many examples in the Bible showing us how to communicate.

In Jeremiah 1:6-9, God tells Jeremiah to *"Go to everyone I send you to and say whatever I command you. Do not be afraid of them, for I am with you and will rescue you"...then the Lord reached out his hand and touched my* [Jeremiah's] *mouth and said to me, "Now, I have put my words in your mouth."*

In Exodus 4:12 God said to Moses, *"Now go; I will help you speak and will teach you what to say."* Paul also credits God with his confidence in speaking, *I came to you in weakness and fear, and with much trembling. My message and my preaching were not with wise and persuasive words, but with a demonstration of the Spirit's power, so that your faith might not rest on men's wisdom, but on God's power* (1 Cor. 2:3-5).

Under our own power we can do very little. However, we can have confidence because God has said through His Word that we can rely on Him. *For the Lord will be your confidence and will keep your foot from being snared* (Prov. 3:26). That's what "Bold Assurance" is about—communicating confidently as we let the Lord speak through us.

Communicating with bold assurance takes bold submission. It is as simple as that and it is as difficult as that. Can we be submissive? Can we receive hope from God by doing what He says? (Jer. 29:11.) Can we give up our hope in ourselves and give it over to Him? (Heb. 12:9.)

In the space on the following page, write of a time when you know that you relied on the power and confidence from God to accomplish a goal.

"For I know the plans I have for you," declares the Lord, "plans to prosper you and not to harm you, plans to give you hope and a future" (Jer. 29:11).

We have all had human fathers who disciplined us and we respected them for it. How much more should we submit to the Father of our spirits and live! (Heb. 12:9).

How do you picture bold assurance? My image is of somebody speaking out with a confidence and certainty about something deep and passionate on his or her heart. People like this are authentic, and they are effective.

We need to have a "Forward Lean" about our communications. I want to give my definition of Forward Lean. It is an expectant mind-set that looks for opportunities. In communicating, someone with a Forward Lean anticipates opportunities to speak, looks for situations to be a positive influence, is always prepared to speak on a moments notice, and strives to communicate with energy and excellence.

The practiced Forward Lean communicator has a focused message with a specific Point of View, is aware of the felt needs of the Listener/audience, provides specific Action Steps, and presents the Benefits to the listener for responding affirmatively to the communicated message.

Let me describe why the term *forward lean* is so vivid for me. It's been many years since I was in the film business, but I still remember one narrative line written for *Robert Kennedy Remembered,* the Academy Award winning documentary that I was privileged to coproduce. It was a phrase describing the newly-elected Senator Robert Kennedy when he arrived in Washington just after his election. The narrator was Richard Burton, and with a powerful voice he said, "Robert Kennedy arrived at the Capitol, hitting the ground, leaning foward." That single line has remained with me, capturing a concept that is simple, yet powerful.

Picture someone with eagerness, energy, and enthusiasm for the job that lays ahead, such as the forward lean of an athlete ready to perform. When we begin volunteering, pushing ourselves a bit, and seeing the increased effectiveness, respect, and self-esteem that come from it, we discover that the rewards of a Forward Lean in our communications are worth more than the risk. But it has to be a Forward Lean under the power of God, not under our own power. That's the way God wants us to live—fully, with a Forward Lean.

We have learned that 95 percent of the time that we try something, we succeed. The alternative is to not try. We are destined to failure if we choose to not try, because 100 percent of the time we don't try, we fail. One hundred percent of the time we let our fear hold us back, we will fail. That's why it makes sense to have a Forward Lean in life.

Forward Lean is an expectant mind-set that looks for opportunities. In communicating, someone with a Forward Lean anticipates opportunities to speak, looks for situations to be a positive influence, is always prepared to speak on a moments notice, and strives to communicate with energy and excellence.

95% of the time you try something, you will succeed.

DAY 2

Nervous Energy

Does the thought of making a speech or giving a presentation at work or church make you nervous? *Communicating with Bold Assurance* isn't just about public speaking, it is about all verbal communications, formal and informal. Whether it is formal public speaking in front of a group, or simply sharing our faith to one person, there's a lot of tension—nervous energy. The problem is: we often hold ourselves back. Why is that? What keeps us from being all that we can be in this most critical area—communicating with effectiveness to the people in our lives? I think the answer is fear.

I think there are several reasons for this. First, fear comes from the psychological "fight or flight" response that occurs in human beings whenever they are confronted by danger. The fight or flight response is good because we want to be able to react quickly to actual danger and either take flight—flee from it—or fight it. This is natural and God gave us this response as a useful tool—but too often we let terror or fear overwhelm us, when it is really adrenaline that could enable us to physically act and perform more effectively.

You might say "fear" is just misapplied adrenaline. It is like the athlete before the championship match. He or she has "fear," that is adrenaline, that gives power and life to the performance. If there is no adrenaline, there is a lesser, flatter performance. So there is a good purpose in applying that fight or flight response appropriately.

We've trained thousands of people, through my company, Decker Communications, and in the "Bold Assurance" program, and I find it to be consistently true that we all tend to have that adrenaline. Nervous energy is good, or it can be good, but it also can block us. All athletes have nervous energy, that adrenaline rush, and so should we when we are speaking, when there's a lot riding on it. Whether it's one person across a desk sharing our faith, or it's running a very important meeting, whether it's a key sales call, or speaking in front of hundreds of people, the nervous energy we have should work for us and not inhibit us. The fear response is appropriate. What we have to do is talk.

Look at the chart in the margin. The greatest fear in this country is the fear of public speaking, of getting up before others and being vulnerable. Is the fear of speaking in front of a group one of your greatest fears?

_____

Many people call their fear shyness and hide behind it. I think that shyness is a sin when we use it to cover our feelings of inadequacy or when we are disobedient to what God wants us to do.

Greatest Fears*

1.	*Speaking*	*41%*
2.	*Heights*	*32%*
3.	*Insects & Bugs*	*22%*
4.	*Financial*	*22%*
5.	*Deep Water*	*22%*
6.	*Sickness*	*19%*
7.	*Death*	*19%*

*From *The Book of Lists*.

Take a look at the chart below which is from a study done by the San Francisco State Business School that indicates how people feel about public speaking. Note the emotion of each stage of speaking.

4 STAGES OF SPEAKING

57%

12%

25%

6%

Occasional

Nonspeaker

Willing

Leader

S. F. State Business School Study: 1985.

For the Lord will be your confidence and will keep your foot from being snared (Prov. 3:26).

1. Nonspeaker: Emotion is terror.
   Behavior tends toward avoidance.
2. Occasional: Emotion is fear.
   Behavior tends toward reluctance.
3. Willing: Emotion is tension.
   Behavior tends toward willingness.
4. Leader: Emotion is stimulation.
   Behavior tends toward eagerness.

In what Stage of Speaking are you?_____

Where do you think you can be?_____

What would it take for you to get there?_____

DAY 3

What Really Counts

When you talk about what counts in communication, people must trust you. But what makes up trust—that believability that you have to have no matter when you're communicating, no matter what you're communicating?

What impacts believability? Professor Albert Mehrabian did research years ago on what impacts believability. His findings are still relevant to communicators. There are three aspects of communication that impact credibility: verbal, vocal, and visual. The verbal, the message itself, is the content of your message. The vocal is the sound of your voice, all aspects of the voice—the resonance, the intonation, the pausing, the nonwords, all aspects of the voice that carry the message. The visual is what people see of you, not necessarily your visual aids, but how people see you.

Which of these is the most important? We are often taught that in speaking, if we just say it, people will get it. But there is a lot of other input from our voice and the visual cues that we communicate. If our vocal and visual block our message—what we want to get across—the verbal will not get across. The numbers in the margin are from Professor Albert Mehrabian's study showing the importance of visual.[1]

The truth is, how a person looks or the way a person says something—regardless of what is being said—causes emotion in others. Especially if there is an inconsistent message.

When you last gave a speech, what percentage of time did you spend preparing your content versus preparing your voice and visual impact? What effect would it have had if you had spent more time on the voice and visual impact?

_____

_____

What impacts believability	
Verbal	*7%*
Vocal	*38%*
Visual	*55%*

DAY 4

First Brain

Psalm 139:14 says, *I praise you because I am fearfully and wonderfully made; your works are wonderful, I know that full well.* The intricacies of the human anatomy were beyond the comprehension of the psalmist, but the truth did not allude him. The human body is a wonder to behold. Neurology, the study of the brain, confirms the insight of the psalmist. Modern research reveals how the brain works in the communication process.

What we call the First Brain is made up of the brain stem and the limbic system, the emotional center. The First Brain serves as a conduit for sending stimulus to the Thinking Brain, which is our analytical brain. All five senses are connected to the First Brain, including the auditory and the visual. All communication passes through the emotional center before being processed to the Thinking Brain. The Thinking Brain is the Cerebral Cortex. All conscious thought takes place within this thin layer of brain cells. The Thinking Brain is the source of rational, conscious thought. It is where we think, create, plan, and make decisions.

You created my inmost being; you knit me together in my mother's womb. I praise you because I am fearfully and wonderfully made; your works are wonderful, I know that full well (Ps. 139:13-14).

First Brain and Thinking Brain Compared

First Brain	Thinking Brain
• Instinctual and Primitive	• Intellectual and Advanced
• Emotional	• Rational
• Preconscious/Unconscious	• Conscious
• Source of instinctive survival responses: hunger, thirst, danger, sex, and parental care.	• Source of thought, memory language, creativity, planning and decision making.

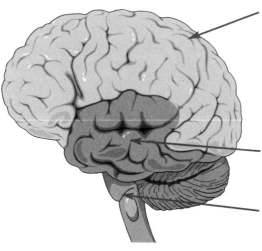

Thinking Brain
The folds of the cerebrum consist of a very thin 1/8-inch thick layer of brain cells called the Cerebral Cortex. All conscious thought takes place within this thin layer of brain cells.

First Brain:
Limbic System, the emotional center

Brain Stem, providing immediate instinctual response

You may be asking yourself, *What is the purpose of all of this First Brain/Thinking Brain information?* Most people who receive training in communication in a high school or college speech class, or in a training seminar, are taught to communicate from an analytical, Thinking Brain perspective. We are taught to develop an outline, a tool of written communication, and logically, analytically develop our thoughts to persuade others. The mind-set is, if we communicate our conscious and rational thoughts in a concise, articulate manner, communication occurs. In communicating with others the goal is to get ideas from our Cerebral Cortex to the listener's Cerebral Cortex. This is true when we are communicating one-to-one or in communicating with a large group.

We presuppose that our ideas go directly from our conscious and rational Thinking Brain to our listeners conscious and rational Thinking Brain. But the reality is all verbal communication passes through the unconscious emotional First Brain first. The implications of this for the communicator are enormous. This is why the vocal and the visual have such a tremendous impact on spoken communication. The brain filters that data along with the verbal message in the communication process. This is why effective speakers make an emotional connection with their audiences whether it is one person, a small group, or a large crowd. We have to reach the listener's heart before we can reach the listener's mind. People buy on emotion and justify with fact. This is the way that God made our brains. The idea of buying on emotion and justifying with fact will be dealt with in more detail in week 2.

Briefly describe the last time you "bought on emotion and justified with fact."

_____

_____

_____

DAY 5

Enthusiasm

I would like for you to think of your favorite high school or college teacher. It's probably the teacher who had the most passion—the person who felt strongly about the subject, and had the most enthusiasm, in turn affecting you, reaching you emotionally. That's how important enthusiasm is. And that's what you want to have in your communications.

What would you say is the age of the most effective communicator? _____ I believe it is two-year-olds. Most two-year-olds have no inhibitions, no fears of speaking or communicating, and they have high energy. They may not be too articulate in what they verbalize, but they effectively communicate what they want!

Do you know what happens to us after two? We lose our effectiveness because we get inhibited. I have a concept called the affect-meter. Affect is your emotional energy. Affect is a feeling level. As two-year-olds, and through early childhood, we tend to have a high affect. Nothing inhibits us. We connect with people, we talk, we move, we feel, we yell, and do all kinds of things to communicate.

What happens is because we do those things, we are told to be quiet, to be seen and not heard, and we begin to get inhibited. But it gets worse. In high school we have peer pressure and we become even more inhibited because we don't want to do anything that's risky. Then, in business or even in church settings, we tend to become even more inhibited because of what is considered correct in the outside world or by other people's standards. The more we are inhibited, the more the affect-meter goes down. That's why we may have low energy and enthusiasm when we are communicating.

I've found that what we need to do is continuously work on our enthusiasm—removing some of that inhibition, so we may connect with others in a way that can really move them. That's why enthusiasm is so important. Without it, our communications are not going to reach the emotional level. Personal contact is imperative: communicating is a

Affect-Meter

30%　　　　70%

0%　　　　　　100%

(1-2 Years)

30%　　　　70%

0%　　　　　　100%

(13-19 Years)

30%　　　　70%

0%　　　　　　100%

(30-50 Years)

Communicating is a contact sport.

contact sport. We have to make contact and connect with a person's emotions if people are going to "get" our message.

In James 1:6 it says, *He must believe and not doubt, because he who doubts is like a wave of the sea, blown and tossed by the wind.* Of course, James is talking about the importance of trust in God. Likewise, when you are communicating, don't doubt, don't fear, don't be inhibited. Have enthusiasm when you communicate. You may not be able to do that of yourself, so let God help you do it. Let Him guide you so you can communicate what's on your heart and in your mind to others. You do that, and you'll be as effective as you can be.

Observe children as they communicate—particularly two-year-olds for natural energy and adolescents for loss of energy. Compare the communication energy of children and adults. List your comparisons on the chart below.

	Children	Adults
Enthusiasm		
Tone/Use of Voice		
Use of Words		
Fear of What Others Think		
Movement		
Expectations		
Others:		

Communication Challenge

- *Identify one of your habits, any habit, and do it differently.*
- *This week, separate the elements of communication and observe others. See who and what gets your attention and makes a connection, and why.*
- *This week I can have a Forward Lean by...*

[1]Albert Mehrabian, *Silent Messages* (Belmont, CA: Wadsworth Publishing Co., 1981).

Session 2:
Visual Impact–Seeing the Big Picture

1. The Written Word vs. the Spoken Word

   If you want to communicate information, do it in _____.

   Do not _____ speeches.

   People buy on _____ and justify with _____.

   Read words to_____. Speak words to_____!

2. Habits

   Maxwell Maltz said it takes _____ days to change a habit.[1]

The Nine Behavioral Skills
1. EYE COMMUNICATION
2. Posture & Movement
3. Dress & Appearance
4. Gestures & Facial Expression
5. Voice & Vocal Variety
6. Language & Nonwords
7. Listener Involvement
8. Humor
9. The Natural Self

[1] Maxwell Maltz, *Psycho-Cybernetics* (Englewood Cliffs, NJ: Prentice-Hall, 1960).

3. Four Learning Stages

    1. _____ Incompetence

    2. _____ Incompetence

    3. _____ Competence

    4. _____ Competence

4. Feedback

The three types of feedback are: _____ , _____ , and _____ .

The 3 x 3 Rule–

    3 _____ , (keepers, things that the person did well);

    3 _____ , (areas that the person could improve).

5. Eye Communication

The three "I's" of eye communication are _____ ,

_____ , and _____ .

If you don't have ____ communication, you don't have communication.

_____ _____ has nothing to do with content, but everything to do with your connection to a person.

1. Why do you think most people read speeches? Do you think reading speeches is a crutch?

2. What surprised you in the information on eye communication?

3. How do you think your eye communication is right now, as you are talking to your group? Do you think others in your group agree with you?

4. For practice using the 3 x 3 Rule, fill out a card on your leader, and give it to your small-group discussion facilitator when you are finished. No names are necessary.

Visual Impact
Seeing the Big Picture

A man's ways are in full view of the Lord.
Proverbs 5:21

How others see you is not always the same as how you perceive yourself. There is a disparity of perception. Although it is good to get that disparity as close as you can, it will never be the same. There is only One who is able to see accurately how you see yourself and how others see you. And that is God. Review what you learned from the video by reviewing pages 21-22 in this Workbook. In the space below, write one habit that you may need to change as a result of balanced feedback.

DAY 1

The Written Word vs. the Spoken Word

There is a difference between writing and speaking. The written word is principally a cognitive process. The spoken word is much more complicated because it adds behavioral impact.

> *In the video, I describe the first speech that I gave when I was in the eleventh grade. I researched, studied, wrote out my cards, memorized, rehearsed—then grabbed the lectern, looked at the audience, and froze! In the space in the margin, write about your first speech.*

Take a closer look at the actual differences between writing and speaking. The written medium is the medium for information. If you want to communicate information, do it in writing. If you want to create action, do it by speaking, because you have multiple things going on and you are connecting emotionally with people. Speaking is multi-channel. Writing is single channel. Writing reaches the Thinking Brain analytically in singular focus, whereas speaking more effectively reaches the First Brain, the emotional brain that helps carry the energy of your message into the Thinking Brain.

I recommend that people do not read speeches. Reading speeches is not the most effective way to communicate. Working from a system that puts ideas together in a way that helps you speak from the heart is more effective. The Decker Grid System is a way to do this. You will learn about that in weeks 4 and 5.

> *Write an explanation of the statement, Writing is single channel and speaking is multichannel, and how it relates to the statements, Read words to inform. Speak words to transform.*

As I mentioned in week 1, people buy on emotion and justify with fact. In using the term, *buy,* I mean they buy into your ideas. They are persuaded. They agree with, that's the buy. When you are communicating, particularly if you are communicating your faith—the most important thing in your life—you really want to influence with your spoken words. That's what I mean by connecting at the emotional level. People buy into your passion and your authenticity, then they will justify with the facts that you give them to agree with your message.

Romans 10:17 says that *Faith comes from hearing the message, and the message is heard through the word of Christ.* Since faith comes through hearing the gospel, it is

Faith comes from hearing the message, and the message is heard through the word of Christ (Rom. 10:17).

critical that we speak that message. That message is the motivation behind our wanting to improve our speaking skills.

> *Is your faith in Jesus Christ the most important thing in your life? Are you passionate and emotional about your faith? Do you show others that you are? If you do, ask God to help you seek out the lost so you can share your faith with them. If you don't show others the importance of your faith, stop right now and evaluate your Christian walk. Is it everything it should be? Ask God to help you be transformed into the believer He wants you to be, and to give you a passion for sharing your faith with others.*

DAY 2

Habits

Communication is made up largely of habits. Here is a quick exercise I would like you to do. Fold your arms in front of you. Just cross your arms. Now, if you can, fold them in the opposite way. You can tell that you have them folded the wrong way, but can anyone else tell which way is the right way? The wrong way makes you feel uncomfortable and you may think everybody can tell it's the wrong way. But generally they can't tell. Here's the point. Every time you change a habit, there's a disparity in it. When you change a habit, you may feel like it is obvious to everyone else, but it is not.

It takes 21 days to change a habit.

According to Maxwell Maltz, it takes 21 days to change a habit. If you wanted to change the habit of folding your arms one way to folding them another way, it would take 21 days of practice to change your habit. Practicing a habit takes time, and if you practice for 21 days then you have a choice. Then if I said, "OK, please cross your arms in front of you," you would ask, "Well, should I do it right over left or left over right?"

> *Do you have the habits of Christian discipline such as Bible study, prayer, and relying on God? Do you have some habits that you need to change? If so, write the habit in the space that you would like to change. Now set a date that you will begin changing/working on that habit for 21 days. Write the date here*

_____.

We are creatures of habit so we need to consider our communication habits. We are aware of bad habits that other people have which prevent them from being effective communicators. We are not as aware of the positive habits others have that make them good communicators, we just say, "Wow, what a great speaker!" This week we will be introduced to the Nine Behavioral Skills. These skills can be learned and with practice can become our habits in communicating. Improving our Behavioral Skills and developing good communication habits will help us connect on a personal level with our audiences.

In week 1 we discussed the fear we feel when we are under pressure. Performance anxiety is closely related to the fear of speaking. Every individual has performance anxiety. We want to perform at our peak level when the pressure is on, without anxiety. But when we are under pressure is when it's the toughest time to speak without anxiety.

It is when the pressure is on that we want to do our best—and it is then, ironically, that our emotions flood our minds. This is why we fall back on old behaviors and habits, and we are not able to think clearly or behave with the confidence that we would otherwise have.

Now that can change. The training you receive in *Communicating with Bold Assurance* gives you a choice. You have a choice about your habits. You can choose confidence over fear when under pressure. You can choose to put your trust in God and rely on Him.

When you rely on God and not on yourself, the pressure eases and you can speak with confidence. I remember one of my biggest moments in giving a speech. It was a case of high-level tension. But I had a sense of calm because I had prayed earlier that morning and turned my speech over to Him. I also remember when I did not know the importance of relying on God and obeying His commands, and how alone I felt and how difficult speeches were for me.

DAY 3

Four Learning Stages

Communicating habits are in the area of Behavioral Skills. The good news is that we can learn the Behavioral Skills and put them into practice in our communication.

There are four learning stages in which you can place the process of changing habits. This comes from a trainers tool and it is the way you learn everything. The first stage is the level of unconscious incompetence. This is the way you learn to ride a bicycle the first time, or drive a car, or give a speech. An example is driving a car. In the unconscious incompetence level, you very consciously concentrate on pushing the gas pedal but fail to release the brake. If you don't know that you don't know something, you are in a stage of unconscious incompetence.

In your own words, write an example of unconscious incompetence that you have experienced or that you have noticed in someone else.

You move from unconscious incompetence to the second stage, the level of conscious incompetence. This stage is where you know that you don't know. For instance, you see yourself on video and say, "Oh, I didn't know I did that. I want to change that habit." Maybe the habit is not looking at the audience, overusing a word, or poor posture. So the work happens between stage two and stage three.

Stage three is at the level of conscious competence. This is where you work at changing the habit. If you are learning to drive a car, you put the car in gear, check your mirrors, push the gas pedal, and learn to coordinate all it takes to drive a car. The same thing happens with all of the communication skills that you are going to learn about.

When was the last time that you worked at changing a habit? Did you feel that when you were changing the habit, you gave more thought and attention to it? Does it come more easily now?

Stage four is at the level of unconscious competence. You don't have to think about these skills. They become internalized, they are part of you. They are your choices—choices about the habits of how you communicate.

What are the four learning stages?

1. _____ Incompetence
2. _____ Incompetence
3. _____ Competence
4. _____ Competence

DAY 4

Feedback

Feedback is critical. We cannot know how our communication skills are without feedback. The 3 x 3 exercise gives us a way to get people feedback. There are three types of feedback: people feedback, audio feedback, and video feedback. People feedback is a tremendous tool that we can use.

Let me describe the 3 x 3 rule for people feedback. The 3 x 3 rule includes three positives, (keepers, three things that the person did well); and three improvements, (areas that the person could improve in their communications). Often the feedback you do hear is vague or general such as, "Oh, you were wonderful," or "Oh, that was awful." It does not help you know what was effective or ineffective. What you need is specific, balanced feedback. The 3x3 forces balanced feedback.

If you get 3 x 3 feedback a lot, as you will in the process of this course, you will discover some things that are good. You do not have to worry about the positives, "You have high energy," or "You don't have a monotone voice," or maybe "You move and use gestures well." You also discover some habits that you were not aware of like, "You don't look at people when you communicate." When you ask for and receive 3 x 3 feedback over a period of time you'll find it is valuable. It doesn't cost anything, you get it immediately, and it can bring to the conscious level what your skills are. I urge you, when you are out with groups and others, to get as much 3 x 3 feedback as you can.

Use the 3 x 3 Coach's Card below as often as you can. Anytime you are speaking, have these cards available for your listeners. By using the Coach's Card, you will be more likely to receive balanced, immediate feedback.

Speaker's Name:_____

Keepers   **Improvements**

•   •

•   •

•   •

Coach's Name:_____

Coach's Card

Make several copies of the Coach's Card. Fill out one card for yourself. What do you think are three keepers and three improvements for yourself? This week as you watch people on TV giving speeches, evaluate them using the Coach's Card.

DAY 5
Eye Communication

Eye communication is the first of The Nine Behavioral Skills. It is the most important skill.

What you want in eye communication is the same thing that you do naturally one-to-one. You want to look at individuals. There are three "*I*'s" for eye communication: *intimacy, intimidation,* and *involvement.* Intimacy is when you look at somebody across a romantic candle-lit dinner for 30 seconds or longer. Intimidation is staring at someone in a threatening way. The third "*I*" is involvement. Connecting with people naturally is roughly five seconds. Five seconds is an arbitrary figure, it could be three, four, six seconds. The way you look at people naturally is you look at somebody, and then you glance away and you look back. That's what you want to do with a large group or a small group. Eye communication is critical in large-group communications and also one-to-one. That's one of the reasons it is the number one communication skill.

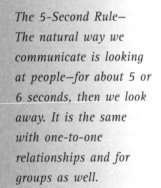

The 5-Second Rule—The natural way we communicate is looking at people—for about 5 or 6 seconds, then we look away. It is the same with one-to-one relationships and for groups as well.

Ask someone to help you with this activity. Ask them to talk to you about their favorite subject for about a minute without stopping. After they have been talking about 30 seconds, look off, look away from them, notice what they do. Now you do the talking for a minute with the other person looking away after about 30 seconds. Answer the questions in the following paragraph.

During the activity, did the energy go up? Did you notice more gestures? More aliveness? How did you feel when you looked away? Did it feel rude? Was it difficult to do? What happened to you when you were talking to somebody and they looked away and you had to continue talking? Did it cause you to hesitate? Did you feel rejected? Did your train of thought seem derailed? The key question is this, How often does that happen in real life? A lot. The real question is, how often are you doing that to others when you are not conscious of it. Somebody is talking to you and you do all the active listening things, you nod your head, say "Uh-huh." But you are looking over their shoulder, possibly nodding to other friends. Do you think there is communication going on?

If you don't have eye communication, you don't have communication. It's the most important skill not only one-to-one, but when speaking to a large group. If you haven't had feedback, then you don't know what your communication skills are. You are unaware that you are not connecting with your listeners. Let me give you an example of poor eye communication. My wife and I visited a church a couple of times where the pastor only looked at two spots on the wall while he preached. I noticed one spot was a stained-glass window on one side of the auditorium and the other spot was a thermostat on the other side of the auditorium. He preached to the stained-glass window and to the thermostat. Now, you wonder how I know that. We sat under the stained-glass window and later we sat under the thermostat, he didn't even look down a little bit. He never looked at the people.

This habit pattern does not work; it reflects a lack of confidence and certainty. An audience is made up of a group of individuals. You've got to make eye contact by looking at individuals in the audience.

Eye communication is critically important in communication. *"The eye is the lamp of the body"* (Matt. 6:22). The eye is dominate in our communications. Be careful of eye dart, slow blink, and the triangle. (See margin.) Your eye communication is vital as it helps you connect with your listener.

> *Have you ever been in a conversation with someone, but felt that even though the person seemed to be listening, you felt like they were not listening? What caused you to feel this way? Was it related to eye communication? Briefly describe your experience in the space below.*

This study is not just about public speaking. It is about small-group and one-to-one communication as well. I mentioned before we have several grandchildren, a couple of them are just over two years old. Do you realize the difference that it makes when you go down on one knee and talk to a child at this level? It is a totally different experience for that child. That's eye communication. It has nothing to do with content, but everything to do with your connection with that person.

This week as you communicate with your family and friends, bring your eye communication skills to the conscious level. How are you looking at people? How are people looking at you? So take that knowledge out with you today. Bring it to the conscious level. Eye communication is the first of the Nine Behavioral Skills. You will see what impact it will have as you communicate this week.

BE CAREFUL OF—

Eye Dart:
Eyes that tend to dart from side-to-side like a scared rabbit, creating a perception of nervousness that undermines credibility.

Slow Blink:
Eyelids closed for up to 2 or 3 seconds, conveying the message, "I really don't want to be here."

The Triangle:
Eye pattern of only looking at the same three people, or the same two or three spots on the wall, when you are talking to a group.

Communication Challenge

- *Spend the next 21 days working on changing a habit that you would like to change. Keep a journal of your struggles and progress as you seek to change the habit.*
- *Increase your sensitivity. Become aware of where you look when you are talking to people. We look at the right or left eye, or nose, or mouth, but we cannot look at "eyes." (Try it—you can't look directly at both eyes at the same time.) Our eyes move around, but they have one dominant spot. If you are not looking at people's eyes, see what happens when you do. Changing your habit may feel awkward to you, but not to the person you are looking at.*
- *This week I can have a Forward Lean by...*

Session 3:
Learning the Behavioral Skills

Energy helps you make the e_____ c_____ so people get what you are going to say. Sometimes our behavior blocks our communications. We want to remember "Don't tighten,_____."

Posture and Movement (#2)

    Use the _____ _____.

    Move out from behind the _____.

Dress and Appearance (#3)

    If in doubt, dress _____ rather than dress _____.

Gestures and Facial Expression (#4)

    Find out what the _____ _____ is that's inhibiting you.

    The _____ is the likability connection.

    The likability connection is not superficial. It's _____.

Voice and Vocal Variety (#5)

Beware of the _____ voice.

Language and Nonwords (#6)

Pausing allows you to _____, as well as getting rid of the nonwords.

The Nine Behavioral Skills
1. Eye Communication
2. POSTURE & MOVEMENT
3. DRESS & APPEARANCE
4. GESTURES & FACIAL EXPRESSION
5. VOICE & VOCAL VARIETY
6. LANGUAGE & NONWORDS
7. Listener Involvement
8. Humor
9. The Natural Self

1. On a scale of 1 to 10, how much are you risking in new communication habits so far? (1 = not at all; 10 = always working at it) And what have been the results?

2. Of the Behavioral Skills talked about so far, which do you think is your weakest and which is your strongest? Would the group agree?

3. Practice pausing. Think of a simple subject and talk to your group, pausing three seconds between each sentence. Then compare your internal feeling with the external reaction of others. (Notice the disparity!)

4. For practice using the 3 x 3 Rule, fill out a Coach's Card on your small-group facilitator, and have one person collect them and hand them to him/her. (No names are necessary.)

Learning the Behavioral Skills

I do not understand what I do. For what I want to do I do not do, but what I hate I do.

Romans 7:15

There are Nine Behavioral Skills that have little to do with content, but lots to do with connection, and everything to do with energy. Each skill can be learned. You need to take a look at your habits and the Behavioral Skills you use, so you can see what you are doing right and see what you need to do to improve. Review what you learned from the video by reading pages 33-34 in this Workbook. In the space below, write one of the Nine Behavioral Skills that you want to improve on this week. Explain one action that you will take to work on your improvement in this area.

DAY 1

Communication Needs Energy

Just imagine this, you are facing three thousand people and you are about to go on stage. You hear the buzz of the crowd, the expectation, the anticipation—are you filled with confidence and ready to flow? Are you ready to hit the zone so that your words and ideas are flowing from your mouth and your energy is flowing through your body? It is tough to do, but that is what you want to be able to do. Unfortunately, in the big speaking situation, when the tension is highest, that is when you tend to tighten the most.

I think there are basically two reasons. The first problem is most people don't know what they do when they are naturally communicating—they don't have the behavior feedback or skill vocabulary that is in *Communicating with Bold Assurance*. And the second problem is that we so often do the opposite of what we should do. I'm reminded of what Paul said in Romans 7:15, *I do not understand what I do. For what I want to do I do not do, but what I hate I do.* If we could speak with confidence and certainty, we wouldn't need to bring to the conscious level the Nine Behavioral Skills. All we would have to do is speak.

If we could see ourselves continuously communicating we would see a lot of positive things that we do in the behavioral areas. We would also see some things that aren't that effective that we would want to change. These are ingrained habits. It is important for us to take a look at our habits. We will be more effective in our communications as far as the behavioral skills go because of our involvement in *Communicating with Bold Assurance*.

> *When we talk about the Nine Behavioral Skills, we are talking about energy. Communication needs energy and if we don't have energy we are not going to get the message across, people will not grasp it, or get into it. List in the margin speakers you have heard that have high energy.*

If we don't have energy, we don't have impact. It is so important to just be ourselves, to be natural with enthusiasm and confidence. Many people go through *Communicating with Bold Assurance* or The Decker Communications training with videotape feedback, and gain confidence because they see themselves. They are better than they thought they were and they gain confidence in themselves.

But the most valuable confidence is not in ourselves, but in God. Jeremiah 17:7 says, *"Blessed is the man who trusts in the Lord, whose confidence is in him."* If we trust God's power to transform our lives, we can trust Him to reach our listeners through us.

"Blessed is the man who trusts in the Lord, whose confidence is in him" (Jer. 17:7).

DAY 2

Posture and Movement
Dress and Appearance

Posture and movement is the energy that we show as people look at us. This includes upper body posture. Obviously we want good upper body posture. If we are slump shouldered, we would tend to have a more difficult time communicating confidence. Remember: perception is reality in the eyes of the beholder.

Upper body posture is important, but I'm talking more about lower body posture. When we get up in front of people, we tend to want to move back, subconsciously, so that the energy is moving away from instead of toward the audience. Or we may rock back and forth, or side-to-side, or hip-to-hip. These habits are not very effective. We want to move our energy out to our audience. So I want to talk about the ready position. The ready position is a concept that will guarantee that we are ready for Forward Lean in our communications. The ready position basically comes from athletics. It gets us ready, ready to move in any direction.

> *I'd like you to try the ready position. Stand up and just bounce on the balls of your feet so that your weight is forward. Now stop bouncing but stay forward so that you could bounce if you had to. Now, that's the ready position. It may feel awkward at first, but it will feel natural with practice.*

The ready position is really effective in your communicating, because it's the base from which you move. If your weight is forward, you literally cannot go back on one hip. Your energy will be physically forward, because when you are leaning forward, you tend to want to go forward. Psychologically that's the forward lean from a physical point of view. If you use the ready position in your communications it will make a world of difference in your energy and the fact that you will reach out to your audience and connect much more effectively.

I urge you to speak from the ready position. With a ready position you are able to have a Forward Lean, you will be able to move forward. That's the movement part of posture and movement.

Movement is important in communicating effectively. It is not very effective to stand in one place while speaking. Too many people speak from behind lecterns. The problem is when we do that it blocks our physical energy. The other problem with lecterns is we tend to grab on to them with our hands. I suggest that we move out from behind lecterns.

We have more capability when we are in a formal speaking situation to change our environment and move out and talk to people. When we communicate effectively we communicate with all of ourselves—our movements, our postures, our bodies, our eyes, our faces and smiles. We want to control the environment. I encourage speakers to do the two step. Some people say, "OK, I'll get out from behind the lectern," and they stand beside the lectern. Others move a half-step, but what we want to do is move two steps.

When you are standing around tonight and tomorrow, practice standing in the ready position. If you make the ready position a habit you'll be more effective in your communicating, because it's a base from which to move. Write in the space below why movement is important when you communicate with others.

Dress and appearance is more important than we think. We want it at our conscious level because how we look has an immediate impact on people. Dress appropriately and comfortably for the event. A lot of people make a statement by the way they are dressed. I find that our dress can be a positive part of our communication. We need to make sure the way we are dressed doesn't stand in the way of what we want to communicate. It's important to think about our dress and appearance as communication skills because too few people put it at the conscious level. There isn't a right or wrong way to dress, but we want to be conscious about what we wear in any setting. If in doubt, we should dress up rather than dress down.

DAY 3

Gestures and Facial Expression

When we are up in front of others we tend to do things with our hands out of habit. Our habits may be comfortable for us, but they are not comfortable to the people we are communicating with. When we use a nervous gesture that is comfortable to us, but not comfortable to the audience they wonder, *Why is he or she doing that?* I've found in my own experience there's about 30 or 40 nervous gestures that people have. I want to describe just a few of them. For example, there is the parade rest—standing fairly rigid, hands clasped in back. Another example is the stern father—arms tightly crossed in front of chest. Some other distracting gestures are the hand wash—rubbing hands in a wringing or washing motion; the pinky pull—the pinky finger is pulled over and over. Some people twirl rings or fiddle with watches or jewelry. Ever heard the jangler? The jangler jangles coins or keys. The most common nervous gesture is what I call the fig leaf—the speaker stands straight, arms down full length with fingers lightly clasped together in front of the body. The fig leaf is literally a cover up. I find about 60 or 70 percent of the people in my seminars have the fig leaf. These distractors are not necessarily at the conscious level, but how irritating, and what a distraction to communications.

Why do people do these things? They are habits at the unconscious level. We really want to know the habits that work against us, then we want to stop doing them. If we are hand washers, we need to pull that up in our consciousness and stop doing it. The 3 x 3 feedback that we get throughout the study will help us know our conscious and unconscious communication habits. Then we can work on not doing those habits. I'm not saying we shouldn't gesture or move, but I am saying get rid of the nervous gestures that are inhibiting our communications. When speaking our hands should be relaxed, at our sides. We should only use gestures that enhance our communications.

Use your 3 x 3 feedback to identify your nervous gestures. If possible, video tape yourself and carefully watch for any nervous gestures.

Let's talk about the smile, the positive facial expression that creates what I call the "likability connection." The smile can be powerful or the lack of a smile can be counter productive to our communications. I have discovered that this one little behavior, smiling, has a tremendous impact on the listener or the audience. When I smile I have a smiling audience. I've found in my own experience with thousands of different people, a top one-third of the people have natural smiles. They are just either born with it or learn it and that's a great asset. The middle third will smile or not as appropriate. The lower third do not smile. I am in the lower third. I might be really excited and feel good but my face doesn't reflect it, I forget to tell my face. A speaker who does not smile, does not make a likability connection. So people will not connect with him. I have learned to smile, and it has become a habit. If we tend to look grim when we are talking to people, then we want to lighten up so we will be able to reflect a friendly face. We will connect more.

The likability connection is one of the most critical skill areas. A smile communicates confidence. As listeners, we like and trust communicators who smile. That's why it is so important for us as Christians to cultivate trust and develop the likability connection. With the smile, along with the other skill areas, we can connect with people and make a difference in their lives. The likability connection is not superficial. It's critical.

DAY 4
Voice and Vocal Variety

Voice and vocal variety is skill number 5. Beware of the monotone voice. I find this to be a critical factor of people who need to have variety in their voice.

We do so much work on the telephone. When we are on the phone we have a big connection with people that is purely from the vocal. Remember in week 1 we discussed the verbal, vocal, and visual? Take away the visual, because on the telephone we have no visual. What is more important in audio communications? Is it verbal—the content of what we say, or vocal—how we sound? The vocal component, the emotional component on the phone of the voice and how the voice sounds is 84 percent of that connection.

Verbal	7%
Vocal	38%
Visual	55%

It's important how your voice sounds for trust and believability. Remember, people buy on emotion and justify with fact. That's the emotional component of the voice. You don't want to have a monotone voice. It is critically important to have energy and show expression. That's voice and vocal variety.

Verbal	16%
Vocal	84%

If you have voice mail, listen to your message. Hear yourself and how your vocal tone is. Do you have energy and expression in your voice? As you hear the voice-mail greetings of others, notice how they use energy and variety in messages. List below or in the margin some areas of voice and vocal variety you plan to improve in your speaking.

DAY 5

Language and Nonwords

Language and nonwords is skill number 6. The pause is a powerful communication tool. I've found a lack of credibility and trust through nonwords where pauses should have been left and they weren't. Nonwords are "uh's" and "aw's." When a speaker uses nonwords, credibility and believability of the message and messenger are lost. We can leave a pause right in the middle of a sentence. As a matter of fact, we can leave a three second pause and not know what we are going to say next. But pausing allows us to determine what we will say next.

Nonwords are very distracting in our communications, particularly on the telephone. But in all our communications we want to replace those nonwords with pauses. The problem is a three-second pause seems like 30 seconds. We need to practice leaving pauses to replace nonwords. As we get comfortable using the pause to replace nonwords, we'll also be able to use the pause to provide dramatic emphasis, or to stop and think when we don't know what we are going to say next. Pausing also allows us time to breathe. A pause will work. That's the power of the pause.

Find out from your voice mail or 3 x 3 feedback if you use nonwords and then leave a three-second pause in place of the nonwords. Write your findings

below and describe how it felt to use a pause in place of your nonwords. How do you think your pause in place of nonwords sounded to your listeners?

I hope the skills you have learned this week, along with eye communication skills, is bringing communication habits to the conscious level. This week as you communicate with others consider the Behavioral Skills you have studied. Notice who is effective and who isn't, determine why communications are working and why some are not working. Bring all these skills to the conscious level.

Most of us undermine ourselves when we fail to trust God and have faith that He will give us the words to say in any circumstance. Trusting God and having faith in Him is a positive step to communicating boldly. You may be asking, *Where does positive thinking come in?* Positive thinking must reflect our faith in Jesus Christ. Norman Vincent Peale was a giant in the communications field. I remember an interview that I had with him a year before his death when we were talking about confidence in speaking and faith. It was in his home on the upper east side of New York City. He said at that time that his greatest book, *The Power of Positive Thinking,* was really meant to be his testimony to the power of Jesus Christ. The interesting thing is when you read the book that is exactly what it is, with Christ and God at the core. So Dr. Peale had some frustration with the fact that people emphasized the surface aspect of his book and that it became known as more of a superficial power of positive thinking. Dr. Peale did not think that positive thinking alone—as helpful as it is—could make a significant difference without the power of God.

Communication Challenge

- *Do the two-step the next time you are talking to a group, move and have someone count the steps.*
- *Smile artificially, for practice only. Try it in the mirror first, then try it on someone and notice what reaction you get. Now, smile at others without it being a phony smile and notice what reaction you get.*
- *Practice pausing on voice mail. Use your voice answering machine for feedback in pausing. Feel the disparity on how awkward it might feel, but how natural it sounds. Do it until your internal feelings more closely match the external perception that you hear.*
- *This week I can have a Forward Lean by...*

Session 4:

Focus—Setting Cornerstones

Focusing Your Message

The next two sessions are about _____ .

Good understanding wins _____ (Prov. 13:15).

The Grid System is a way to help us _____.

Three Message Problems

They tend to be_____. They tend to be _____.

They tend to be _____.

Two Key Tools

The first tool is _____-_____. (Placed upside down.)

The second tool is _____ _____.

THE SPIRITUAL CORNERSTONES

1. POINT OF VIEW
"Run in such a way as to get the prize. Everyone who competes in the games goes into strict training. They do it to get a crown that will not last; but we do it to get a crown that will last forever. Therefore I do not run like a man running aimlessly."
1 Corinthians 9:24–26

4. BENEFITS
"Do not let any unwholesome talk come out of your mouths, but only what is helpful for building others up according to their needs, that it may benefit those who listen."
Ephesians 4:29

2. LISTENERS
"To the weak I became weak, to win the weak. I have become all things to all men so that by all possible means I might save some. I do all this for the sake of the gospel, that I may share in its blessings."
1 Corinthians 9:22–23

3. ACTION STEP
"Faith without deeds is dead"
James 2:26

"Do not merely listen to the word, and so deceive yourselves. Do what it says.
James 1:22

The Most Important Step: Cornerstones

SUBJECT

1. POINT OF VIEW
(POV)
FOCUS

Your feeling, opinion, and attitude about the subject

4. BENEFITS

The Benefits YOUR LISTENERS will receive from taking your Action Step(s)

(List three Benefits)

2. LISTENERS

1. Who are they?
2. What do they know about the subject?
3. How do they feel about the subject?

3. ACTION STEP

1. General Action Step
2. Specific Action Step (Physical, measurable, time oriented)

DELIVERING THE CORNERSTONES

When delivering your Cornerstones,
you will simply:

1. State your Point of View (POV).

POINT OF VIEW
(POV)

*Your feeling, opinion and attitude
about the subject*

2. Tell people the Action Step.

ACTION STEP

1. General Action Step
2. Specific Action Step
   (Physical, measurable, realistic)

3. Give them one or more Benefits.

BENEFITS

*The Benefits YOUR Listeners will
receive from taking your Action
Step(s)*

(List three Benefits)

(You drop the "Listener" Cornerstone when you
speak because you no longer need it—it was for
mind-set only.) Place your Post-its on this page
for the Small-Group exercise.

1. Share with your group how God has been working in your life this past week.

2. Make a stand-up presentation to your group of the Cornerstones you created in class. Take one to two minutes. Although you may be concentrating on content, remember to use eye communication and energy. You want feedback on both style and substance. Remember to applaud everyone after they are done. Just doing it deserves applause.

3. After each presentation, fill out a 3 x 3 Coach's Card. The prime areas to consider are the behaviors we discussed in the last two class sessions, plus clarity and point of view from this session. Add whatever else occurs to you that will be helpful. Fill out the cards immediately, but only give them out after the last person has spoken.

4. If time permits, have each person share an instance of Forward Lean they used last week.

Focus–
Setting Cornerstones

Good understanding wins favor.

Proverbs 13:15

In the first three weeks of *Communicating with Bold Assurance* you learned about six Behavioral Skills. Weeks four and five are about content. What you want to do is get your content, your message to your audience. The key to effectively communicating content is focus. Focus is knowing exactly what you want to say and doing so. Focus makes your communications interesting and clear. By using the four Cornerstones you will find your focus in 80% of your communicating situations. As you go through the Workbook this week, follow the directions for using the Decker Grid System. Use Post-its and trigger words as directed. Fill in the Cornerstones with your subject, Listener information, specific Action Step, and the Benefits. Review what you learned from the video by reading pages 43-45 in this Workbook. In the space below, write how God has been using what you have learned thus far from this study.

Focus and the Grid System

Proverbs 4:7 says: *Get wisdom. Though it cost all you have, get understanding.* In *Communicating with Bold Assurance,* we urge you to not only get wisdom, but to use it well. This week you will be introduced to the Decker Grid System™, which will help you create and organize your thoughts so that you can communicate clearly. Focusing your message is the theme of this week. Too often you see and hear people giving lessons and presentations with a lot of information, but little focus and clarity.

There are three potential problem areas in communications that have a lot of content. The first is somebody who has a point, but uses a lot of words to make it. The problem is they tend to be boring. The second problem is the person who is interesting, but tends to ramble. They go over here, they have a great story over there, it really sounds good but it doesn't have anything to do with the point they are trying to make. Ramblers may have a point, but it takes them twice as long to make it. They may have entertained you in the process, but it's not effective communications, because it's not focused. The third problem is the person whose communication is pointless. The speaker may be entertaining but when finished, the listener asks, "What was that about?" Communications that are boring, rambling, or pointless have one thing in common: a lack of focus.

Have you thought about your communications? Is it possible you tend to be boring, rambling, or pointless in your communications? If so, circle your problem area and write one reason why you think this is your problem.

There is a solution to these problem areas: the Decker Grid System. The Decker Grid System is a practical, common-sense approach to developing a presentation that has focus. The first step of the four-step grid system is laying the Cornerstones. When talking or speaking you have a subject. This is the topic of your presentation. The four Cornerstones are how you develop your thoughts on any given subject with focus and clarity. Next week we will discover the other steps: Create, Cluster, and Compose.

Two primary tools used in the Decker Grid are trigger words and Post-its®. A trigger word is a word or a group of words that represent an idea or concept about which we could speak for 30 seconds to five minutes. In this process we write our trigger words on Post-its, one word or one idea per Post-it. The reason we use Post-its is because they are movable. The beauty of trigger words on Post-its is you can quickly rearrange, delete, and add to your presentation grid. You can order your Post-its very quickly because you can move the ideas around. This is simple, but I think you will find it extremely useful.

Get wisdom. Though it cost all you have, get understanding (Prov. 4:7).

DAY 2

Point Of View (POV)

Point of View is probably the most important cornerstone because it establishes your focus. You start with your focus. Point of View is your feeling and opinion about the subject, it is your emotional focus. How do you feel about the subject? What is your passion? What do you want to accomplish? Usually your Point of View has an active oriented word in it. Your Point of View is your mind-set. It is what you want to get across to people. Your Point of View should answer the "so what" question for the listener. The listener may not agree with you, but they get your point. They know it is important to you and they know there is a reason to listen to you.

Once you have your Point of View, then your ideas about what to say will be attracted to it like a magnet. If your ideas are bathed in wisdom from framing, forming, and molding your thinking with the Bible, then your Point of View will likely be a wise one.

I am convinced there is a scriptural foundation for each one of the four Cornerstone steps. The biblical basis for establishing your Point of View is 1 Corinthians 9:24-26, *Run in such a way as to get the prize. Everyone who competes in the games goes into strict training. They do it to get a crown that will not last; but we do it to get a crown that will last forever. Therefore I do not run like a man running aimlessly.* Paul's passion never wavered from his commitment to Christ. He was always focused. This passage captures that focus. We want to be that way as Christians serving God intently, any time we give presentations, any time we communicate.

In the verse in the margin, circle the active words that Paul used to describe his passion, his mind-set, his emotional focus. Stop right now and ask God to keep your focus on Him. How will this focus help you with your Point of View as you develop the first Cornerstone?

Run in such a way as to get the prize. Everyone who competes in the games goes into strict training. They do it to get a crown that will not last; but we do it to get a crown that will last forever. Therefore I do not run like a man running aimlessly (1 Cor. 9:24-26).

DAY 3

Listener

The second Cornerstone is—Listeners. In laying this Cornerstone it is important to put ourselves in the shoes of the listener so we can create listener-based messages. This forces us to consider where they are coming from so we can strike a responsive chord.

Speech classes teach you to know your audience. The focus is on demographics, social, economic, male, female, etc. You want to know who your listener group is. But you also want to go beyond that. How much do you care about them and how they will receive your message? How do they feel about the subject. Are they resistant? Are they hostile? Are they for it or are they neutral? How do they feel about you? Where are they coming from? If somebody is hostile to your message about Jesus Christ, you need to know that, you need to know their spiritual temperature. You need to know your listener group.

Think of a specific listener group, or person that you could be speaking to. For example, it might be your Sunday School class. It might be a civic club. It might be speaking to somebody in a family setting. Make it a specific listener group so you can care about them and know in your mind what they feel about the subject and about you. How might this effect your presentation?

To the weak I became weak, to win the weak. I have become all things to all men so that by all possible means I might save some. I do all this for the sake of the gospel, that I may share in its blessings (1 Cor. 9:22-23).

The scriptural basis for considering your listeners is found in 1 Corinthians 9:22-23 when Paul said: *To the weak I became weak, to win the weak. I have become all things to all men so that by all possible means I might save some. I do all this for the sake of the gospel, that I may share in its blessings.* Paul did whatever he had to do to identify with his audience. He never compromised the message, but he always framed it to the listener group he was talking to. That's what you want to do.

DAY 4
Action Step

The third Cornerstone is Action Step. You want to advocate an Action Step for your listeners to take. Too often there is no closure because you do not suggest what the listeners should do as a response to the message. This is probably the most neglected step when putting together thoughts for communications. The problem with presenting ideas without an Action Step is the audience can say OK, and not do anything with the message. They are just kind of nodding and going along rather than doing something.

You want a specific Action Step so people will do something that is physical, measurable, and time oriented. State what you would like them to do specifically, something they would not do otherwise. Have your listener write something down. That is physical. You want an Action Step that is specific, physical, measurable, so push yourself to think of something that would be specific. When you give a specific Action Step, they may not do it. But you are pushing them to do it, so if they agree with your Point of View they will consider doing something. That's why you want it specific. Here is an example: *I'd like you to take a piece of paper and write this down on it: Read Proverbs daily.* They may not do it, but it's specific, it's physical, and it's measurable. They are going to have to decide right there if they are going to write that down and do it.

I gave you an example of a specific action to get your listeners to do. In the space below, write a few more examples of specific actions. As you write, ask yourself, Is it specific, is it physical, is it measurable? Use one in your Grid.

A scriptural basis for advocating an Action Step is James 2:26, *Faith without deeds is dead.* Knowing the gospel is of no use if someone does not live the gospel. Faith is important. True faith always leads to action. We want to move our listeners to deeds, to action. We want them to hear our message and do something. James 1:22-25 says, *Do not merely listen to the word, and so deceive yourselves. Do what it says. Anyone who listens to the word but does not do what it says is like a man who looks at his face in a mirror and, after looking at himself, goes away and immediately forgets what he looks like. But the man who looks intently into the perfect law that gives freedom, and continues to do this, not forgetting what he has heard, but doing it—he will be blessed in what he does.* Being doers as well as hearers is a pattern that we can apply to life.

If you have a concept and you communicate it with passion, you are focused, but if you don't suggest an Action Step you are not likely to get a response. Ask your audience to hear you and do something that is specific, physical, and measurable.

Faith without deeds is dead (Jas. 2:26).

Do not merely listen to the word, and so deceive yourselves. Do what it says. Anyone who listens to the word but does not do what it says is like a man who looks at his face in a mirror and, after looking at himself, goes away and immediately forgets what he looks like. But the man who looks intently into the perfect law that gives freedom, and continues to do this, not forgetting what he has heard, but doing it—he will be blessed in what he does (Jas. 1:22-25).

DAY 5

Benefits

The fourth Cornerstone is Benefits. You want to clearly state the Benefits to the listener. If listeners don't see the Benefit, they are less likely to accomplish the Action Step. I recommend advocating three Benefits to your listener or listeners.

The biblical basis for establishing Benefits for your listeners as a Cornerstone is found in Ephesians 4:29: *Do not let any unwholesome talk come out of your mouths, but only what is helpful for building others up according to their needs, that it may benefit those who listen.* The benefits are critical to whoever is in your audience.

As you talk or make your presentation the listener is asking one simple question: "What's in it for me?" Make sure you state the Benefits for your hearer. Again I recommend writing three specific Benefits on three separate Post-its for the Benefit Cornerstone. If you are sharing your faith and your testimony, which is one of the main purposes of *Communicating with Bold Assurance*, you want to tell people what's in it for them, the Benefits of becoming a follower of Jesus.

Do not let any unwholesome talk come out of your mouths, but only what is helpful for building others up according to their needs, that it may benefit those who listen (Eph. 4:29).

List below three Benefits of becoming a Christian. Use these in your Grid.
1.

2.

3.

Conclusion/Wrap-up

The four Cornerstones are: 1. Point of View; 2. Listener/Audience; 3. Action Steps; and, 4. Benefits. Here is the order for delivering the Cornerstones:

(1) State your Point of View.

(2) Give your Action Step.

(3) State Benefits for Listener.

Omit the Listener Cornerstone because it was just for the creative process. Next week we will discuss how you will add stories, examples, and details to your presentation. The Cornerstones are the foundation of your presentation. The benefit of setting your Cornerstones is that you will have a focus.

Good understanding wins favor (Prov. 13:15).

The overall biblical principle behind the four Cornerstones is found in Proverbs 13:15, *Good understanding wins favor.* When you have good understanding of what needs to be accomplished, the message will win favor with the audience. When you have good understanding of what they need and want, and establish the Benefits for them with specific Action Steps they can take, then the message wins favor, and will be received and applied. The communicator who gets results is the one who listens to God's wisdom, is focused on his or her message, has a strong Point of View, sends a listener-based message with specific Action Steps, and clearly communicates the Benefits to the person or persons they are talking to.

Communication Challenge

- *Use the Cornerstones process once each day this week. It's simple and there are many ways the Cornerstones can be used. For instance:*
  - ➤ *Planning a Bible study or Sunday School lesson*
  - ➤ *Organizing a memo or letter*
  - ➤ *Before making a key phone call or leaving a voice mail*
  - ➤ *Preparing for a sales call*
  - ➤ *Making an important decision*
  - ➤ *Planning a meeting*
- *Read back over this entire week (pp. 43-52) to reinforce the Cornerstone process.*
- *This week I can have a Forward Lean by...*

Session 5:

1. Cornerstones

Take the Post-its that you did in Session 4 (p. 44) in Setting Corner-stones and place them on this page, preparing for the Create, Cluster, and Compose Steps on the following pages.

1. Point of View
(POV)

Your feeling, opinion, and attitude about the subject

4. Benefits

The Benefits YOUR LISTENERS will receive from taking your Action Step(s)

(List three Benefits)

2. Listeners

1. Who are they?
2. What do they know about the subject?
3. How do they feel about the subject?

3. Action Step

1. General Action Step
2. Specific Action Step (Physical, measurable, time oriented)

53

2. & 3. Create and Cluster

Use this page for the Create and Cluster Steps

4. Compose

(Opening and the Delivery Order)

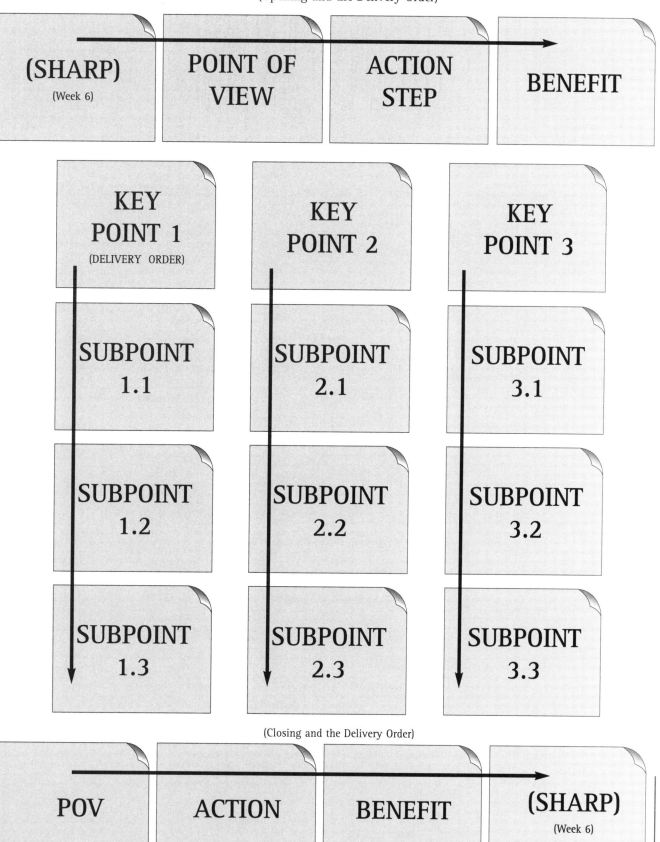

| (SHARP) (Week 6) | POINT OF VIEW | ACTION STEP | BENEFIT |

| KEY POINT 1 (DELIVERY ORDER) | KEY POINT 2 | KEY POINT 3 |

| SUBPOINT 1.1 | SUBPOINT 2.1 | SUBPOINT 3.1 |

| SUBPOINT 1.2 | SUBPOINT 2.2 | SUBPOINT 3.2 |

| SUBPOINT 1.3 | SUBPOINT 2.3 | SUBPOINT 3.3 |

(Closing and the Delivery Order)

| POV | ACTION | BENEFIT | (SHARP) (Week 6) |

1. Share with your group how God has been working in your life this past week.

2. Make a stand-up presentation to your small group of the ideas you created in class with the Grid process. Take 2–3 minutes. Although you will be concentrating on content, remember to use eye communication and energy–you want feedback on both style and substance.

3. After each presentation, fill out a 3 x 3 Coach's Card for that member. Consider Behavioral Skills: eye communication, pausing, and energy particularly. Consider content: Is there a strong Point of View, Action Step, and Benefit? Consider overall effectiveness. Fill out the cards immediately, but only give them out after the last person has spoken.

4. If there's time, each of you share with the group an instance of Forward Lean you have made during the week.

Creating and Organizing Ideas–Quickly

"My teaching is not my own. It comes from him who sent me...He who speaks on his own does so to gain honor for himself, but he who works for the honor of the one who sent him is a man of truth; there is nothing false about him."

John 7:16,18

In every situation, seek God's help. Keep your mind and heart saturated with the Truth from the Bible. Seek His power and bold assurance in tough situations. Ask Him to give you His words to say to others. Words are powerful. Review what you learned from the video by reviewing pages 53-55 in this Workbook. This week as you work through the Workbook, follow the instructions for building on the Cornerstones. Create and organize your ideas quickly as you use the Grid. Write in the space below of any possible opportunities you may have this week to practice using the Decker Grid System™. Now, seek out those opportunities and practice!

DAY 1

Powerful Words

This week we will do the second half of the Decker Grid System. What we did last week was lay the Cornerstones. This week we are going to build on the Cornerstones by Creating, Clustering, and Composing our ideas. Initially we developed the Decker Grid System so people could put their ideas together quickly, but we found this is the best way to put together ideas because of the way the mind works. The Grid System helps us when creating spontaneously, the way the mind works naturally. When Creating, Clustering, and Composing we are brainstorming, using our minds to access quickly those best ideas that are top-of-mind. We organize them and add to them, using the words and ideas that first occur to us.

I want to encourage you to have the best top-of-mind ideas: the Word of God. Saturate your mind with the Bible, so that His Words are the words or ideas that first occur to you. I want to share three things I have learned to do, so that my mind is saturated with God's Word. First, a major agent of spiritual transformation is reading the Bible daily. I pray for God to help me understand the spiritual truth in the Bible, and to apply the ideas from His Word as I am communicating. Second, I use the Bible as my guide. This helps me pattern my life after Jesus, in turn helping me choose my words carefully. Third, I pray God's Words from the Bible and it helps me begin to choose the right words—very often God's own Words.

When you read the Bible daily, let the Bible be your daily guide, and pray the words from the Bible, you will discover that these words will be at the forefront of your mind. These are the words your mind goes to automatically. When the Scriptures become your trigger words, you will know you have chosen the right source for your words. My prayer is that God will transform you into the likeness of Jesus and transform your communications through your focus on His Word.

My Plan

1.

2.

3.

Write in the margin a plan for saturating your mind with God's Word.

DAY 2

Create

The Create Step develops out of the Cornerstones. Start with your Cornerstones because these are the ideas that are the foundation of your presentation. In the Create Step, use your mind naturally, the creative way that God made your mind. You will work quickly—your mind moves at breakneck speed to choose the right trigger words that connect with the Cornerstones and write them on Post-its. Many of these words are content words—facts and figures, concepts and ideas—but they are the words that are top-of-mind—words that your mind goes to automatically.

The principle of brainstorming is the essence of the creative process. When brainstorming don't edit, don't censor. You want as many ideas as possible. You want quantity, not quality.

Give yourself a time limit when you do the Create Step. The reason you want a time limit is you want your mind forced into a time spectrum so you get as many ideas out as you can. So give yourself a time limit. Set a time limit of five minutes, ten minutes at the maximum. Get all of your ideas on the page with Post-its upside down, just a trigger word or two. This is the base from which you will work.

The creative process does not stop arbitrarily. It will continue on. So as you go through the rest of the processes, feel free to add Post-its, because the creative process is continuous. That is the way your mind is made. In five minutes you will be amazed at the number of ideas you have. This is the natural process. You now have a template from which to work. That's the creative process.

Now use your Cornerstones on page 53 to begin the Create Step on page 54. Brainstorm using the process in the above paragraphs. Set a time limit and write down trigger words that connect with your Cornerstones as quickly as you can.

DAY 3

Cluster

The Create Step is followed by the Cluster Step. Basically, this step involves organizing the ideas that come out of the Create Step. What you are going to do is cluster all of your ideas in natural groupings. All of your ideas are on the page. You begin by grouping these ideas naturally. The way to Cluster is to take the Create and Cluster page (p. 54) and just take any Post-it, any idea that you have, put it up in a corner and say, What matches that? What's a kind of natural grouping? Then you underline your Key Points.

This is a fast process and you should end up with three, four, or five different groupings. You may find that you have just one idea that stands alone. That's fine. You may want to use it later. This is the clustering process.

On page 54 practice clustering your ideas so they are in natural clusters. Review Day 3 for additional help with the Cluster step.

DAY 4

Compose

Now you are ready to move to the Compose Step. This is the easiest part because it is the editing process. Now you will be able to pick the best ideas for your presentation.

Avoid Data Dumps

There are two bits of advice to consider in the Compose process. One is avoid data dumps. In business that's just a lot of facts, information, and figures without a point. Be careful of just giving a lot of facts and figures. In Christian presentations, data dumps can be multiple Scripture references without a point. Scripture works fine but when you are speaking, you want to make sure you have a point with it and an application for it. So, be careful of data dumps, of overloading people with facts, figures, and information. Then, you want to use the K.I.S.S. principle: Keep It Simple Sweetheart. The main thing is, keep it simple. The Compose process is getting it down to just those key points.

Keep It Simple

These are the basic principles of the Compose process. In my training seminars I walk participants through this process. Let me give you some of the highlights of that training. In the Compose process, take the ideas in these natural clusters and go to the Compose page. You have the Cornerstone page, Create/Cluster page, and then the Compose page (55). You are going to end up with just 12 Post-its on the Compose page. Now you may have 20 Post-its to deal with. You have a lot of different ideas, so you have to edit. On the Compose page, focus on the 12 boxes in the middle, this is the body of your presentation. (The opening and closing will be added later.) You want to take the best three Key Points from your Cluster page and put them in the boxes labeled Key Point 1, 2, and 3. Then take the three best Subpoints from those Key Points and list those underneath. Compose your ideas so you end up with 12 Post-its in the body of your presentation.

The Compose process gives you a basic template for the body of your presentation, three Key Points and the three Subpoints, the best ideas from the creating and clustering process. It is not intended to lock you into always having three Key Points with three Subpoints. You may have two Key Points or four Key Points. You may have two Subpoints under one of the Key Points and four Subpoints under another Key Point. The Compose process is a template, but the "rule of three," three Key Points and three Subpoints, works. I do recommend that you use this model in its present form as you practice the Grid System for presentations. Then feel free to adapt it when necessary in future presentations.

Next you want to develop the opening. You will see the opening across the top of your Compose page. Notice the horizontal order that you go in across the page [→]. Take your Point of View Post-it that you did on the Cornerstones page and put it in the box labeled Point of View. Then take your Action Step Post-it. If you have two Action Steps—a general action step and a specific, take the general action step. If you just have one, place it in the Action Step box. Save your best Benefit for the closing and move the second best Benefit Post-it in the Benefit box. That's going to be your opening. Remember the old adage, "Tell them what you are going to say, say it, and tell them what you said." Well, you are going to tell them what you are going to say. Give them your Point of View, an Action Step, and a Benefit. They'll be interested, and then you go to your body starting with Point 1 with Subpoints, Point 2 with Subpoints, Point 3 with Subpoints.

Next develop your closing. Take a blank Post-it, put it in the bottom Point of View box and write your Point of View again. Repeating your Point of View is a good idea, it is worth repeating. If you have a second specific Action Step, put that down in the Action box, or repeat the Action Step from your opening if you have only one specific Action Step. Save your best Benefit to last and place it in the Benefit box. That will be your closing. You close with, "This is my Point of View, this is what I want you to do, and this is what's in it for you."

Use the above information to compose your presentation on page 55. If you have already set your Cornerstones, created, clustered, and composed a presentation using the Grid, pick another POV and practice using the Grid Method again. The process becomes easier and more comfortable with practice.

DAY 5

Putting It Together

That is the Grid System in very quick form. Turn to the Compose page (55). Take a look at what you have there. This is not necessarily a perfect presentation, it's not necessarily a complete presentation, but it is a very effective one, as you will see that when you deliver it. The beauty is it came from the natural creativity in your mind.

Let me just add one interesting and very valuable thought for you about delivery. Because the beauty of the Grid Process is when you have ideas on Post-its, you have your Grid, and you can be talking to somebody or to a group and you forget the second point down from the second Key Point. But you know where it is on the page and all you have to do is pause. When you are in control, there's nothing wrong with pausing and glancing at notes.

Using the Grid is a great way to deliver because you've prepared it in a way that is much faster. It takes half the preparation time compared to writing it out. It works the way the mind works and it's great for delivery because you can just pick up each key word, off the page. Remember this, you will want to say every idea on your page, but you may forget some. And you'll think to yourself, *Oh, I forgot that idea!* The reality is nobody missed that idea. If you did your presentation and they got the Action Step and they bought into what you wanted to get across, that's all you need. The audience only gets what you give them. It can be profound when you internalize that and realize they don't have your script, they don't know what you intended to say. This gives you freedom to not worry too much about missing a point.

Plan a time you can deliver your presentation to a group or individual. If you delivered it during your small group, present it to someone else for practice.

The king's heart is in the hand of the Lord; he directs it like a watercourse wherever he pleases (Prov. 21:1)

We talked earlier about reading the Bible, being immersed in the Word. It is important to have the right stuff in our hearts and in our minds and to get it out to people in a natural way. If we do that, we will have done what God wants us to do because He directs us. *The king's heart is in the hand of the Lord; he directs it like a watercourse wherever he pleases* (Prov. 21:1). He will give us the right words. This is a natural process and I think the Grid will help you a lot when you are communicating. Try these ideas out. If you have a presentation coming up, use this Grid Process, try it, see if it works for you. Then you will be communicating with bold assurance.

Communication Challenge

- *Use the feedback you received to polish your initial presentation.*
- *Use the Grid system to create and deliver another presentation. Remember to ask for 3 x 3 feedback.*
- *This week I can have a Forward Lean by...*

Session 6:

Communicating Heart-to-Heart

You have to reach the_____ to reach the mind.

Use the SHARP principles—

S_____

H_____

A_____

R_____

p_____

Like a _____, you are creative.

The Nine Behavioral Skills

1. Eye Communication

2. Posture & Movement

3. Dress & Appearance

4. Gestures & Facial
   Expression

5. Voice & Vocal Variety

6. Language & Nonwords

7. LISTENER INVOLVEMENT

8. HUMOR

9. The Natural Self

---

1. Share with the group how you have had success saturating your heart and mind with words from the Bible.

2. Tell a story. Each person think of a story of a memorable experience. It might be a vacation, a sporting triumph or defeat, a celebration, a completion or overcoming a job challenge. The first one that comes to mind usually works best. Then deliver it as one of the SHARP principles—best done presenting it. Tell the group your story. Take one to two minutes each, then give each person 3 x 3 feedback on Coach's Cards.

3. We are going to do a group process of feedback, encouragement, and sharing. This is a powerful exercise that is called "The Love Game." It is actually not a game but feedback that is true and accurate, and will inspire you to continue in a Forward Lean mode. Start with the person on the facilitator's right who will be "It." Then starting with the facilitator and going left, each person will give one or two positive comments, true things they like or admire about the person who is "It." After you have gone around the circle, the next person on the right is "It," and so on until complete. Each comment should be about a minute or less. The only other rule to the game is that the person who is "It" must not deflect or diminish the positive comments, but just acknowledge and accept them.

Communicating Heart-to-Heart

Above all else, guard your heart, for it is the wellspring of life.

Proverbs 4:23

Speaking to the heart is the central theme this week. You need to speak to the heart of your audience, whether it is one person or a thousand people. You will never get to someone's mind without getting to his or her heart first. Emphasis on the heart is throughout the Bible and it has to be your emphasis when you communicate. Review what you learned from the video by reviewing page 63 in this Workbook. In the space below, write from memory the Behavioral Skills you have learned during this study. Pick one of the skills and briefly describe how it has helped you in your communications.

The Heart

The first three weeks of *Communicating with Bold Assurance* was primarily about Behavioral Skills. Weeks four and five focused on content, using the Decker Grid System. This week we will unite Behavioral Skills and content. We want content and behavior that connects us with our audience. We must reach the hearts of our audience before we can reach their minds. The theme of this session is on the heart.

If you were sitting in an auditorium and someone walked to the center of the stage and started to talk, you might be like me and ask yourself, *Why should I listen? Why should I learn from this person?* When most people are speaking, they typically think others should learn from them because of what they know, their content, but that is not what comes first. We are trained from our academic background that the rational facts are everything. All we have to do is communicate the facts and figures, and people will get them. As we have seen from earlier sessions—this is just not so.

The heart is the key. We have to speak to the hearts of our audience. We will never get to the mind of somebody without getting to their heart first. It is just that simple.

"Come to me, all you who are weary and burdened, and I will give you rest. Take my yoke upon you and learn from me, for I am gentle and humble in heart, and you will find rest for your souls."
Matthew 11:28-29

Read Matthew 11:28-29. When Jesus invited the weary and burdened to come to Him, notice the reason that they could learn from Him. Why should we learn from Him?

Notice that Jesus did not frame His invitation by saying, learn from Me because of My mind. He said, *"Learn from me, for I am gentle and humble in heart."* With God, the heart comes first. In the Great Commandment Jesus said, *"Love the Lord your God with all your heart and with all your soul and with all your mind"* (Matt. 22:37). So what does it mean when the Bible refers to "heart"?

In week 1, the concept of the First Brain was introduced. I think the First Brain is what God is referring to when He talks about the heart. It has to involve more than the physical heart muscle. Our emotional powerplant is the First Brain. It colors all of our thoughts and is central to our desires, wants, needs, and attitudes. It is also very important in our communications.

We talked about connecting with people with the Behavioral Skills, such as eye communication, movement, gestures, and smiling. When we connect personally with people they will buy into what we say. That's the behavior side. The content is just as important. Content is the best ideas of our mind which are clustered and composed using the

Grid System. It takes a lot more than just content to reach the heart. Reaching the heart is our objective, because if we fail, we miss an opportunity to communicate. The best way to communicate to affect people on a heart level is by telling our stories, giving our testimonies, or by sharing our faith.

The SHARP Principles are Behavioral Skills that will help us connect with the hearts of our listeners. **SHARP** is an acronym: S for Stories, H for Humor, A for Analogies, R for References and Quotes, and P for Pictures and Visuals. That is what we want to do in our formal communications, but also in our informal, everyday communications. SHARP Principles are the practical application of how we connect with the hearts of our listeners. The SHARP Principles are listener-involving techniques that can be learned. Listener Involvement is one of the Nine Behavioral Skills. You can develop these Behavioral Skills. Remember, when you want to communicate with people, start with the heart, touch people's hearts.

S tories
H umor
A nalogies
R eferences &
 Quotes
P ictures & Visuals

You will enjoy better acceptance, better connections, and better relationships when you practice the SHARP Principles. Jesus is our supreme model in *Communicating with Bold Assurance.* He was an amazing example for reaching the hearts of His audiences with His use of parables and analogies. Jesus spoke continuously using picturesque images and stories. We have no better communications model for reaching the hearts of listeners than Jesus.

DAY 2

The S in SHARP: Stories

Stories is the first acronym of the SHARP Principle. It is probably the most important of the SHARP Principles because stories are tremendous communication tools. Stories breathe life into a presentation. A good story is vivid, you can picture it, you can visualize it. Stories are wonderful tools for application. Jesus was a great storyteller, and He did much of His teaching through stories and parables.

He then began to speak to them in parables (Mark 12:1). Throughout Jesus' ministry in the Gospels, we read parable after parable, story after story, memorable and insightful parables, dramatic and picturable stories. Most of the stories and parables that Jesus told created visual images. For instance the parable of The Good Samaritan, *"A man was going down from Jerusalem to Jericho, when he fell into the hands of robbers...."* (Luke 10:30-36); and The Prodigal Son, *"There was a man who had two sons...."* (Luke 15:11-31); and many others, *"A farmer went out to sow..."* (Mark 4:3-8); *"If a man owns a hundred sheep..."* (Matt. 18:12-13). These stories bring Jesus' teachings to life. If you want understanding—use parables. If you want memorability—use stories.

He then began to speak to them in parables (Mark 12:1).

Stories are powerful, but many of us tend to shy away from using stories in our communications. I urge you to reverse this trend, think of stories for your presentations. Don't throw out the stories when your time is shortened. Remember, stories connect with people at the heart level. A story's content has application and it connects.

Practice storytelling whenever you have an opportunity. Read a short story then practice retelling it. Use the Grid to determine the critical points of the story. Then retell it using the Grid and the Behavioral Skills.

DAY 3

The H in SHARP: Humor

Humor is the eighth Behavioral Skill and it is the toughest to teach because not that many people are naturally funny. By humor I do not mean just telling jokes. It is OK to start a speech with a joke or use jokes if you are a good joke teller, but most people are not. Use humor in your presentations, but remember humor is more than telling jokes.

Two tips will help you be more humorous. One is to think funny. Put a template in your mind, a framework of thinking funny. When you are trying to create or when you are doing a grid in a creative process, think *what's the twist I can have here*. The second tip is to keep a humor notebook. Write down the things that make you laugh or smile. Use these in your communications whether it's one-to-one, or whether it's to a group.

Humor is humanization, making yourself part of the human comedy, it's taking your subject seriously, but taking yourself lightly. Stories and asides about yourself help you connect with people. The likability connection is really important.

Practice using humor. It is a very important SHARP Principle and it is very important for the likability connection. Remember to smile. This is so important. Listeners do not relate well with serious people who are grim. It doesn't mean that when something is serious that you take it lightly. You want to be appropriate to the situation. I have been to funerals where a light touch of humor was used. Some of the most poignant moments in funerals reflect the memory of somebody that made people laugh and brought them joy. That's what humor is about.

Earlier I suggested that you keep a humor notebook. Begin the process now by writing in the space below or in the margin, the things that make you laugh or smile and any funny situations or circumstances that you have had. You can later transfer this information to a humor notebook.

DAY 4

The A in SHARP: Analogies;
The R in SHARP: References
or Quotes

Analogies is the A in SHARP. In the Book of Proverbs there are many analogies, many things that are "like" something else. I obviously have a great love for the Book of Proverbs and have mentioned numerous quotes from it throughout *Communicating with Bold Assurance*. Some examples from Proverbs are:

- *A gentle tongue can break a bone (Prov. 25:15).*
- *The lips of the righteous nourish many (Prov. 10:21).*
- *Like a coating of glaze over earthenware are fervent lips with an evil heart (Prov. 26:23).*
- *The king's heart is in the hand of the Lord; he directs it like a watercourse wherever he pleases (Prov. 21:1).*

What better way to visualize and make memorable a concept than to make an analogous comparison. Learn to use analogies, metaphors, and similes where possible when you are communicating with others.

> *Make the analogy/simile connection! Do this exercise in less than 30 seconds. Use this concept: "Faith today..." Make up an analogy of that concept with a cup of coffee. (Example: Faith today is like a strong cup of coffee—once you drink it in it can be strong enough to carry you through the day.) Now make up an analogy of that concept with a rose. Write your analogy here:*

References or Quotes, the R in SHARP

The R in SHARP is for references or quotes. In *Communicating with Bold Assurance* there are many scriptural references and quotes of well-known people. References to data, figures, and statistics are interesting little energy twists used to involve the audience. When you make a specific reference or quote, it is important to apply it. You can also express certain ideas in your Grid better with SHARP Principles. References and quotes are good interludes in any communication, so sprinkle them throughout your communications.

The Bible is not only the standard of truth, even Jesus' enemies, including Satan, recognized it as truth. Jesus used Old Testament quotes many times when He was teach-

Analogy = something familiar (usually concrete) is used to explain something that is unfamiliar (usually abstract), or a similarity between things that are not usually associated. (Example: The radiant heart that loves, trusts, and obeys God is a beacon to the lost.)

Simile = The comparison of two dissimilar things using like or as. (Example: As shrewd as snakes and as innocent as doves.)

Metaphor = comparison between dissimilar things without using like or as. (Example: His heart is a garden for unity.)

ing. Perhaps best known is His reaction in to Satan's temptations. In Matthew 4:4, Jesus said, *"It is written: 'Man does not live on bread alone, but on every word that comes from the mouth of God.'"* The second time He answered Satan's temptation, He responded in Matthew 4:7, *"It is also written: 'Do not put the Lord your God to the test.'"* and again quoted from the Old Testament. When Satan tempted Him again, Jesus once more quoted from the Scriptures in Matthew 4:10, *"It is written: 'Worship the Lord your God, and serve him only.'"*

> *Quote your favorite Bible verse. List Scriptures you have memorized. List Scripture references that are especially meaningful to you, and note why those truths have stuck with you.*

DAY 5

The P in SHARP: Pictures and Visuals

The P in the SHARP Principles is pictures and visuals. People connect visually. We dealt with the importance of visuals in communications in weeks 1 and 2, but I'd like to just make two important points about visuals. One, keep it simple. You don't need complex visuals. You don't necessarily need electronic presentations, though they are effective. You can use demonstrations and props in your presentations. Make visuals that are bold, brilliant, and colorful. The Bible is a rich source of visual representations. Two, learn from the example of Jesus Himself, because He didn't have visual aids and computers like we use today, so He used picturesque language.

> In Matthew 6:26, *"Look at the birds of the air; they do not sow or reap or store away in barns, and yet your heavenly Father feeds them. Are you not much more valuable than they?"* And in verses 28-30 Jesus says, *"And why do you worry about clothes? See how the lilies of the field grow. They do not labor or spin. Yet I tell you that not even Solomon in all his splendor was dressed like one of these. If that is how God clothes the grass of the field, which is here today and tomorrow is thrown into the fire, will he not much more clothe you, O you of little faith?"*

Today you can use all kinds of visual aids plus picturesque language. Your communications will be more effective if you learn to use both.

More than anything else, the SHARP Principles can spice up your presentation and help you connect with people. If you use all of the SHARP Principles wisely, your content will reach the heart. If you just go from point to point to point in your content, you will not be involving people as effectively as you need to. That's why Listener Involvement is a key element in communication.

Do you know the attention span of a child? The attention span of a child is six seconds. What is the attention span of an adult? It is about eight seconds, just two seconds longer than children. That means you have to constantly keep people involved in your communications; otherwise, they are not going to get your message. If you use the SHARP Principles, you will keep your listeners involved.

Last week when you put your opening together on the Compose page (p. 55), there was a box for a SHARP Principle. Open your presentations with something that grabs peoples' attention—a story, a quote, a visual. You should also close your presentation with a SHARP Principle, something that grabs peoples' attention—a story, a quote, a visual. Also look for places to sprinkle SHARP Principles throughout your presentation. If a SHARP Principle can be used to communicate a concept you have in your presentation, for instance a trigger word that is a Subpoint, write the SHARP on a Post-it and place the SHARP Post-it in place of the trigger word. When you say that SHARP Principle, perhaps it's a story, it will automatically remind you of the concept you wanted to talk about. Including SHARP Principles throughout your presentations will help you connect with people's hearts.

Flip back to the Compose page (p. 55) you worked on earlier. This time, review your content and come up with SHARP Principles for the opening and closing of your presentation. List below the kinds of SHARP Principles you used—Stories; Humor; Analogies; References or quotes; Pictures and visuals.

I'd like to close this session with an example from the Bible that illustrates the SHARP Principle. It is a passage filled with SHARP principles, with picturesque language, stories and analogies. The theme of James 3:3-6 is the tongue, so this relates to what we were talking about in communications, the power of the tongue.

When we put bits into the mouths of horses to make them obey us, we can turn the whole animal. Or take ships as an example. Although they are so large and are driven by strong winds, they are steered by a very small rudder wherever the pilot wants to go. Likewise the tongue is a small part of the body, but it makes great boasts. Consider what a great forest is set on fire by a small spark. The tongue also is a fire (Jas. 3:3-6).

List the examples of SHARP Principles in James 3:3-6.

Proverbs 22:11 says, *He who loves a pure heart, whose speech is gracious will have the king for his friend.* If you have a pure heart, your speech will be gracious and you will effectively communicate with others. That is what you want to do. Use the SHARP Principles to reach the hearts of your listeners. God wants to use you to touch the hearts of people through your communication. Let your words honor Him.

Communication Challenge

- *Practice analogies this week. Think of one of the points from your Grid and link it to the first thing you see as you look around you. Try it! You'll find that you can almost always link one thing to another in just a few seconds. We are creative when we allow our minds to flow naturally.*
- *Use stories this week. Push yourself to begin using stories in conversations and presentations more often. Take abstract concepts and principles and link them with a personal story. Practice stories and anecdotes to be more adept at storytelling. Remember that Jesus frequently used stories and parables when He spoke.*
- *Think of the heart in two ways:*
  - a. *Note sometime this week when your "willful heart" is at work. And notice the role God gives to obedience in having reign over your "willful heart."*
  - b. *Use "heart" in your relationships. Take the extra time to communicate to someone that you love them. Forgive someone who is hard to forgive. Think of the compassion God has toward us, and lean your heart towards someone who does not deserve your compassion. Tell someone how this felt.*
- *This week I can have a Forward Lean by...*

Session 7:
Communicating as a Leader

Start this session with the Quick Grid. Your leader will give you instructions.
Purpose: To quickly organize and deliver your ideas. It provides a shortcut in preparation.
Benefits: You will see how creative and fast you are as you quickly lay the cornerstones and choose your key points.
The following process should be done **quickly,** no more than a minute; when finished, go to the next page.

1. Write your Point of View about your subject on a Post-it and place it in the POV square.
2. Think of your audience, no need to write a Post-it—this is just to set your mind.
3. Write on a Post-it an action you want your audience to take and place it on the Action Step square.
4. Write a benefit(s) for the audience if they do your Action Step—place the Post-it on the Benefits square.

SUBJECT

1. Point of View
(POV)
Focus

Your feeling, opinion, and attitude about the subject

4. Benefits

The Benefits YOUR LISTENERS will receive from taking your Action Step(s)

(List three Benefits)

2. Listeners

1. Who are they?
2. What do they know about the subject?
3. How do they feel about the subject?

3. Action Step

1. General Action Step
2. Specific Action Step (Physical, measurable, time oriented)

5. Place your Point of View, Action Step, and Benefits Post-its at the top of this page for your "opening" and at the bottom duplicate Post-its for your Action Step and Benefits (or another Benefit) for the closing.
6. Make up three Key Points and support your POV and place them in the boxes (quickly), and then if you have time make up a few Subpoints or so for each Key Point and place them. You are done!
7. Deliver your talk, following the order given by the direction of the arrows.

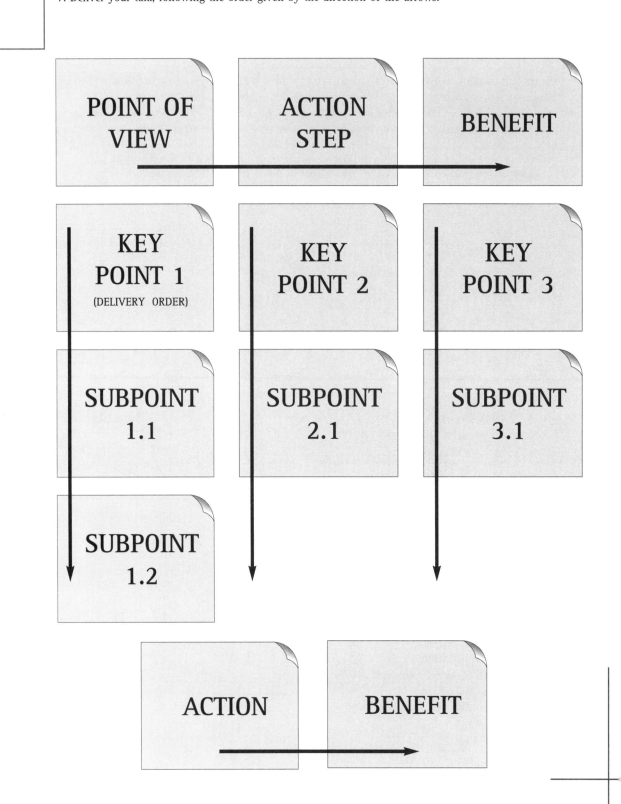

The effectiveness of your _____ determines the effectiveness of your life.

1. God wants us all to be _____.

2. Communication is the primary _____ of leadership.
   Leaders are not _____.

3. Leaders require feedback:
   _____ are always in school.
   Three types of feedback:
   P_____
   A_____
   V_____

   Video feedback is the most _____ feedback.

1. Take the Quick Grid that you did at the beginning of class, and present it to your group. Do it standing, and take no more than two minutes. Try to make sure you have a story or analogy in it. Then each person will practice giving you honest and supportive coaching by giving the 3 x 3 verbally. Have this verbal feedback right after each presentation. Take less than a minute with each person's 3 x 3 feedback.

2. What Stage of Speaking are you in? Do you consider yourself a leader? If so, why? If not, why not? Do you think that God wants you to accept more responsibility in your sphere of influence? What has God shown you?

3. If time allows share your answers to these thoughts with your group:

    • Over the last seven weeks, with what change in your communication skills are you most pleased?

    • Whom in this class, besides the leader, has helped you enjoy more bold assurance in your communications?

    • In which class participants have you noticed the most improvement in speaking with bold assurance? Why?

Communicating as a Leader

Listen, my sons, to a father's instruction; pay attention and gain understanding. I give you sound learning, so do not forsake my teaching. When I was a boy in my father's house, still tender, and an only child of my mother, he taught me and said, "Lay hold of my words with all your heart; keep my commands and you will live. Get wisdom, get understanding; do not forget my words or swerve from them. Do not forsake wisdom, and she will protect you; love her, and she will watch over you."

Proverbs 4:1-6

Communication is the primary tool of leadership. Effective leaders communicate differently than others and their skills can be learned. As you develop your leadership skills, God can use you to influence more people for the cause of Christ. Review what you learned from the video by reviewing page 75 in this Workbook. In the space below, write a brief explanation of three leadership needs and why these are important.

1. Wisdom—

2. Listening—

3. Feedback—

DAY 1

Leadership

I believe God wants all believers to be leaders. Leading is influencing, helping guide people in the right direction. Some leaders are called on to speak to crowds of hundreds or thousands, while others communicate best one-to-one or in small groups. Communication is the primary tool of leadership and *Communicating with Bold Assurance* can help leaders and potential leaders develop the skills necessary to influence others.

The concept of Forward Lean is critically important to leaders, both physically and psychologically. The image of Forward Lean, of coming into a situation and hitting the ground leaning forward, resonates in my mind because I see it in successful leaders. Leaders have an attitude of Forward Lean about life, they take responsibility for themselves and take responsibility for others. A leader who communicates with a Forward Lean makes a difference in the lives of others.

Communicating with Bold Assurance is about communicating and seeing truth make a difference in other people's lives. *What* we communicate is important. *How* we communicate is crucial. Communicating God's truth to people is how we make a difference in our world and it is how we can be used in the kingdom of God. Communication is a critical issue for leaders.

The character of a leader is a hot leadership topic today. It is important that we establish that the measure of Christian character is the degree to which we are like Jesus. He is our standard. As Christian leaders become more like Jesus, we have the opportunity to influence many people. My hope is that Christian leaders will be transformed by God into the likeness of Jesus (2 Cor. 3:18) and communicate God's love in their spheres of influence. Jesus not only serves as our model for communication; He is also our example to follow in leadership. Jesus taught that a Kingdom leader is a servant. He taught (Mark 10:35-45) and modeled servant leadership for His disciples (John 13:3-17). When a person chooses to follow a biblical model of servant leadership as a leader, God will work in amazing ways through that leader.[1]

"For even the Son of Man did not come to be served, but to serve, and to give his life as a ransom for many" (Mark 10:45).

How would you evaluate yourself as a leader? How are you letting God use you to influence other people?

DAY 2

Leaders Need Wisdom

In Matthew 10:16, Jesus sent out the disciples for the first time. He said many things to them, but the one phrase that stands out in my mind is when He told them, *"Be as shrewd as snakes and as innocent as doves."* This is a powerful verse.

I find many Christians emphasize being as innocent as doves, and neglect being shrewd. In other words, there is a lot of grace and love in our churches and ministries, but not enough emphasis on being wise in our dealings. Being wise as a serpent is just as important as being *"innocent as doves."* Effective leaders blend being innocent and being shrewd.

Leaders need to make wise judgments and decisions about people and still be loving and gracious. Too often in Christian circles, in the name of love, excellence is not our standard! Mediocrity is allowed, even accepted. A common example of this is the way churches deal with personnel problems with paid staff or volunteers. I find leaders often do not have the desire or ability to make the hard decisions. Ultimately this blocks their leadership. Leaders need to always show grace and love, but also need to have a high standard of effectiveness, excellence, and accountability. Leaders need to be excellent in all that they do.

Romans 16:19b says, *Be wise about what is good, and innocent about what is evil.* Leader's need God's wisdom, because without it we won't know what to do. Shortly after Solomon became king of Israel, God came to him in a dream and said, *"Ask for whatever you want me to give you"* (1 Kings 3:5). In response, the young king asked God to give him a *"discerning heart to govern your people and to distinguish between right and wrong"* (1 Kings 3:9). God granted that request and King Solomon became the wisest man who ever lived. That same wisdom is available to us. James 1:5 says, *If any of you lacks wisdom, he should ask God, who gives generously to all without finding fault, and it will be given to him.* With God's wisdom we will grow and mature and make better judgments as we lead and influence others.

Consciously seek to have a Forward Lean as a leader. Always be graceful and loving to those that you are dealing with. Ask God for wisdom and He will give it to you. Place your whole confidence in God and see how effectively He will prepare and use you.

Are you placing your confidence in God? List the ways you see that He is preparing you for His service.

"I am sending you out like sheep among wolves. Therefore be as shrewd as snakes and as innocent as doves" (Matt. 10:16).

I want you to be wise about what is good and innocent about what is evil (Rom. 16:19).

DAY 3

Leaders Listen

Leaders listen in a variety of ways, but the most important type of listening is listening to God. Effective leaders make themselves available to listen to God so they will hear what He wants them to do. Jesus is our model of how to listen to God. He prayed to His Father, communicating with Him sometimes all night (Luke 6:12). Jesus then went out and obeyed all the Father had commanded. The leadership principle we learn from Jesus is the importance of going to God for guidance and wisdom.

Jesus went out to a mountainside to pray, and spent the night praying to God (Luke 6:12).

Leaders also listen to the wise counsel of others. We see that in the biblical leadership example of Moses. Moses had a difficult time responding to all of the demands of the people until he listened to the wise counsel of his father-in-law, Jethro.

> *"What you are doing is not good. You and these people who come to you will only wear yourselves out. The work is too heavy for you; you cannot handle it alone. Listen now to me and I will give you some advice, and may God be with you." ...Moses listened to his father-in-law and did everything he said. He chose capable men from all Israel and made them leaders of the people, officials over thousands, hundreds, fifties and tens. They served as judges for the people at all times. The difficult cases they brought to Moses, but the simple ones they decided themselves* (Ex. 18:17-19,24-26).

How wise Moses was to listen to the advice given to him by his father-in-law. Based on Jethro's counsel, Moses selected capable, God-fearing, trustworthy men to serve as leaders. Moses is an excellent biblical model of leadership.

Listening to others is a vital skill for leaders to develop. From more than 30 years of experience in communications and leadership, I find that listening skills play a great role in the success of people who are effective and have the most positive influence. Wise leaders listen to others and get wise counsel. King Solomon said, *Plans fail for lack of counsel, but with many advisers they succeed* (Prov. 15:22). "Lone Rangers" don't make effective leaders.

Plans fail for lack of counsel, but with many advisers they succeed (Prov. 15:22).

Finally, effective leaders listen to their peers and to the people they are influencing and serving. To do this, a skill we need to develop is asking questions. Questions such as: How are people doing in your area of influence? What are their concerns? What are their needs? Listening to our peers, and the people we supervise and influence, can help us know how to communicate with them better. And, while we're at it, listening to our spouses and to our children will lead to healthier and happier families.

God has placed us where we are and He provides the resources we need to serve Him. We learn when we listen to God and when we listen to others. A leader with Forward Lean is an active listener. When we listen to godly counsel from mentors, leaders, people who give us the benefit of their experience and apply it to our lives, we are wise. Proverbs 12:15 reminds us, *The way of the fool seems right to him, but a wise man listens to advice.*

Are you making yourself available to listen to God and to what He wants you to do? Are you listening to your peers and the people you influence? List examples of each in the space below or in the margin.

> *The way of the fool seems right to him, but a wise man listens to advice (Prov. 12:15).*

DAY 4

Leaders Experience Spiritual Transformation

I've found that truly effective Christian leaders are experiencing spiritual transformation. Specifically, transformed leaders have the following four characteristics.

Transformed leaders are disciplined. Practicing spiritual discipline is very important for all Christians, but especially for leaders. Spiritual disciplines are exercises that train us for godliness. Examples of spiritual disciplines are prayer, Bible study, fasting, worship, evangelism, service, stewardship. These spiritual exercises "are the means by which we place ourselves before God for Him to work in us."[2] God can use any of these disciplines as a training exercise to transform us into the likeness of Jesus. The key to remember is that the activity of the discipline is not intended to gauge spiritually, but to create an avenue that God can use to lead believers straight to His heart.[3]

Transformed leaders are focused. They seem to have an incredible ability to focus on what God wants them to do. Many leaders develop personal purpose statements or mission statements to help them stay focused. It is like having a personal Point of View for their lives. How we arrive at our purpose statement or goals is critical. As Christians, especially as Christian leaders, it is essential that we seek the heart of God so that His goals are our goals. Proverbs 3:5-6 says, *Trust in the Lord with all your heart and lean not on your own understanding; in all your ways acknowledge him, and he will make your paths straight.* When God is the author of our purpose statements, our goal-setting process, everything changes. Some people plan and set goals and then as an after thought pray and ask God to bless their work. We need to reverse the order and call upon God before we plan and set goals so that He guides us and makes our paths straight.

> *Trust in the Lord with all your heart and lean not on your own understanding; in all your ways acknowledge him, and he will make your paths straight (Prov. 3:5-6).*

Transformed leaders have self-control. Self-control is a fruit of the spirit. *But the fruit of the Spirit is love, joy, peace, patience, kindness, goodness, faithfulness, gentleness and self-control* (Gal. 5:22-23). Self-control is a spiritual fruit that results when we are under the control of the Holy Spirit. We must demonstrate self-control to be effective leaders. Otherwise, we will not be credible and our leadership influence will be diminished.

Transformed leaders guard their hearts. Proverbs 4:23 says, *Above all else, guard your heart, for it is the wellspring of life.* This is so important for the communications of a leader because Jesus said, *"For out of the overflow of the heart the mouth speaks"* (Matt. 12:34). Jesus went on to say *"that men will have to give account on the day of judgment for every careless word they have spoken"* (Matt. 12:36).

Finally a word of warning. I find that many leaders use sarcasm as a means of communicating. If you want God to use you effectively, don't use sarcasm. When you use sarcasm, people aren't sure you mean what you say. A key ingredient in leadership is trust; sarcasm builds mistrust. You want to be trusted immediately by people so they know you are speaking the truth in love. Your followers need to sense that they can trust you, so be careful of sarcasm.

In the space below write your personal purpose statement or specific goals you have as a leader. If you do not have a purpose statement or any specific goals, use this space to begin developing them.

DAY 5

Leaders Listen to Feedback

Professionals are always in school. For instance, professional athletes have coaches and they practice year round. I find in my business that very few people practice as much as they could or should in communications, and the same thing is true in Christian circles. The effectiveness of our communications can determine the effectiveness of our lives.

Feedback is a fundamental coaching tool of leaders. The feedback of others can make us more effective in our communications and more effective as leaders. It is important that our feedback be balanced. That is why I recommend using the 3x3 feedback process. *Honest scales and balances are from the Lord; all the weights in the bag are of his making* (Prov. 16:11). People feedback is valuable, it is easy, and it doesn't cost anything. If we get in a pattern of receiving balanced feedback we get a good sense of how we come across to others.

3 x 3 Feedback Rule
3 positives
   (keepers, three things the person did well)
3 improvements
   (three areas the person could improve upon)

Audio feedback is another feedback tool. You need to know how you sound to others. What better way to find out than to listen to an audio recording of yourself? The voice is critically important in many different settings. In week two we looked at voice and vocal variety as one of the Nine Behavioral Skills. We discovered that when hearing is the only method used to evaluate a message, 84 percent of the impact is determined by the voice. When I listen to myself on voice mail, I often hear a monotone voice. So, I say to myself, *Bert, get a little lighter, use the roller coaster, go up and down.* Audio feedback is powerful.

If you use voice mail, dial in to your phone and leave yourself a voice mail message similar to one you would leave for someone else. Listen to your own messages every day for a week. This allows you to hear how your voice sounds. You will hear the resonance, the energy or the lack of energy in your voice. You may learn that you have a monotone voice, or that you use nonwords. Do that for a week and then experiment with the Behavioral Skills. Do something different like leaving a three-second pause in the place of nonwords. It may seem like 30 seconds at first, but soon you'll find that it sounds pretty good. Also audio record yourself when giving a presentation or a Bible study so you can hear your voice.

The most powerful form of feedback is video feedback. It is the most powerful because it allows you to observe your behavior. You do not see yourself as others see you. The only way you can do that is through video. Set up a camera in the back of a room when you are doing a training session or when you are leading a group. Then watch the tape and grade yourself on how well you use the Nine Behavioral Skills. You'll be amazed at what happens when you see yourself on video.

In week 1 we had a chart on the Four Stages of Speaking (p. 16). Twelve percent of the people were nonspeakers, terrified at the thought of speaking. Fifty-seven percent were occasional speakers who experienced fear. Twenty-five percent were willing speakers, and they experienced tension. Leaders, at six percent, were stimulated by the opportunity to speak. People at the terror and fear levels are not going to have a strong sense of confidence and generally they are not going to speak with confidence and certainty.

There was a survey done by San Francisco State Business School on how the Stages of Speaking changed after videotape feedback. Decker Communications was involved in this experiment. Participants placed themselves in one of the four catagories (see chart next page). They then went through a two-day program with extensive video feedback. Every person was videotaped 10 times in that program. After going through the video feedback process they filled out the chart again. The results were amazing as you can see in the following two charts.

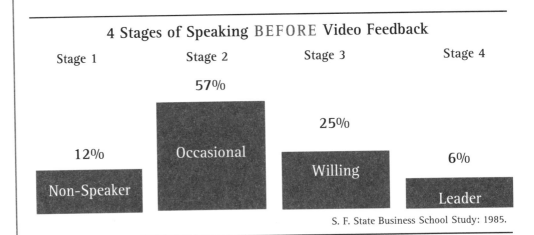

4 Stages of Speaking BEFORE Video Feedback

Stage 1   Stage 2   Stage 3   Stage 4

57%
Occasional

25%
Willing

12%
Non-Speaker

6%
Leader

S. F. State Business School Study: 1985.

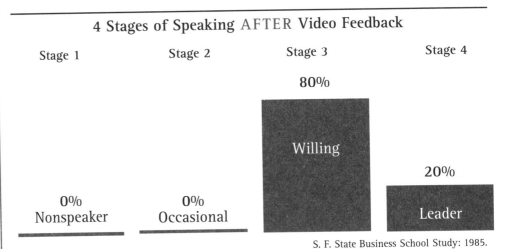

4 Stages of Speaking AFTER Video Feedback

Stage 1   Stage 2   Stage 3   Stage 4

80%
Willing

20%
Leader

0%
Nonspeaker

0%
Occasional

S. F. State Business School Study: 1985.

What makes video feedback so powerful is you see yourself. The first time you see yourself you may be self-conscious, and you may focus on the negatives. However, when you see yourself multiple times, you will begin to see your positive traits. When that happens, it is invaluable because you will then begin to emphasize the positives. Video feedback also allows you to see your communication habits that are distracting so you can work on specific things to improve your delivery. I urge you to do whatever you have to do to get video feedback.

Are you at Stage 4 in the 4 Stages of Speaking that we've talked about? Are you at that place where you have adrenaline pumping when the pressure is on as you talk with another individual, or give a major speech in front of hundreds of people? I wish for you to get to Stage Four because that is the behavior of the most effective leader. Seek to improve your communications so that you will be at Stage Four.

When you consider your leadership, be shrewd as snakes and as innocent as doves. Listen to God and to wise counsel of others. Stay in the spiritual disciplines, stay focused on your purpose, have self-control, and guard your heart. Eliminate sarcasm from your speech patterns. Get people, audio, and video feedback whenever possible.

Sow a thought, and you reap an act, sow an act, and you reap a habit, sow a habit, and you reap a character, sow a character, and you reap a destiny.
—Samuel Smiles

If you are not at the Stage of Speaking that you would like to be, set a goal to be at that Stage by a certain date. Write the date below. In the space, list some specific steps you can take to improve your communications so that you will be at the Stage you desire by the date below.

Communication Challenge

- *Get on videotape this week. If you don't have a camcorder ask around to see if someone is willing to videotape you or loan you their camcorder for a few days or check area stores to see if they will rent you a camcorder.*
- *Write down at least three communication goals here that you will work on this week. Be as specific as you can:*

    1. _____
    _____
    2. _____
    _____
    3. _____
    _____

- *This week I can have a Forward Lean by...*

[1] C. Gene Wilkes, *Jesus on Leadership, Becoming a Servant Leader* (Nashville: LifeWay Press, 1996) 4.

[2] *Spiritual Transformation*, June 10, 1998 © LifeWay Christian Resources of the Southern Baptist Convention.

[3] Barry Sneed and Roy Edgemon, *Transformational Discipleship* (Nashville: LifeWay Press, 1996) 4, 31-32.

Session 8:

The Power of Testimony

Sharing Yourselves with Others

Sharing your _____ with others is the reason for bold assurance.

How to Share Yourself with Others

Give _____, _____, or a faith _____.

Be able to give testimony in _____minute to _____minutes.

> **The Nine Behavioral Skills**
> 1. Eye Communication
> 2. Posture & Movement
> 3. Dress & Appearance
> 4. Gestures & Facial Expression
> 5. Voice & Vocal Variety
> 6. Language & Nonwords
> 7. Listener Involvement
> 8. Humor
> 9. THE NATURAL SELF

How to Tell Your Story

Three things to tell:

1. What your life _____ _____.

2. What _____.

3. What your life is _____ _____.

Your Story

**Christ Can
Change Your
Life**
(He Did Mine!)

(Point of View)

**1. Hope
2. Peace
3. Joy**

(Benefits)

**A Group
of Seekers**
(or an individual)

(Listeners)

• **Go to Church (or)**
• **Join a Bible Study (or)**
• **Accept Christ**

(Action)

Instructions:

1. Put a Post-it in the POV box that says something like, "Christ can change your life!"
2. Consider your audience: are they open, interested, hostile, uninformed? Place a couple of Post-its.
3. Think of one Action you can get them to take—perhaps just to ask questions, or to go to church with you.
4. Think of the three Benefits to them, and write them on separate Post-its.

(The above process should be done quickly, no more than a minute. Then go to the next page.)

Telling Your Story Grid

POV BOX	ACTION STEP BOX	BENEFIT BOX

WHAT YOUR LIFE WAS LIKE	WHAT HAPPENED	WHAT YOUR LIFE IS LIKE NOW
SUBPOINT 1.1	SUBPOINT 2.1	SUBPOINT 3.1
SUBPOINT 1.2	SUBPOINT 2.2	SUBPOINT 3.2
SUBPOINT 1.3	SUBPOINT 2.3	SUBPOINT 3.3

POV BOX	ACTION STEP BOX	BENEFIT BOX

5. Use the regular Grid process you learned earlier, but modify it by starting the Create Step with the three Key Points (noted below) of What Life Was Like. What Happened, and What Life is Like Now. Do this on a separate paper or table top, do the Create, Cluster, and Compose Grid process around each point, and put your best ideas/Post-its on this page under each Key Point and Subpoint.

6. Place your POV, Action Step, and Benefits Post-its at the top and bottom of this page in the shadowed boxes. Thus you can use this one page for all of your delivery.

7. Deliver your talk, following the order given by the direction of the arrows.

1. Share with your group your reaction to Bert's testimony.

2. Prepare to use the Telling Your Story Grid on pages 87-88 of the Workbook. The Cornerstones and outline are the same, but your story is unique. Use the instructions on pages 87-88 to see how easy it is to put your story together. Spend 15 minutes using the Grid System to develop your story.

3. Share your story with others in your small group. This is a good time to share how Jesus changed your life with a friendly, understanding audience. It is great preparation for when you have the opportunity to share the story of your transformed life with someone who is not a Christian. You will have about 5 minutes to share your story. You can do this standing. Place your Telling Your Story Grid on the lectern or chair near you.

The Power of Testimony

"'Love the Lord your God with all your heart and with all your soul and with all your mind.' This is the first and greatest commandment. And the second is like it: 'Love your neighbor as yourself.'"

Matthew 22:37-39

You may have a dramatic story of the change in your life after accepting Jesus Christ as your Lord and Savior, or you may have made that decision as a young child. Either way, you have a life that has been transformed, and it is that life you want to share with others. Remember that Jesus Christ is the only person that truly and permanently transforms lives, and sharing how that happened in your life will bless others and they may also see their need to have Jesus Christ as their Lord and Savior. Review what you learned from the video by reviewing pages 86-88 in this Workbook. Continue to develop your story so you can present it to others. In the space below, write the three things you want to include when you are giving your testimony.

DAY 1

Natural Self

I make a living training people in the corporate world to communicate effectively, but my passion is training Christians to communicate effectively their faith. As Christians we have the most important message—the gospel of Jesus Christ. Since this is true, we as believers need to be trained to share our story, our testimony, so that we can influence others who need to know Jesus. The purpose of this session is learning to share ourselves. Sharing our hope with others is the reason for communicating with bold assurance.

You will find unique opportunities to share your faith, if you are open to it. First Peter 3:15, *But in your hearts set apart Christ as Lord. Always be prepared to give an answer to everyone who asks you to give the reason for the hope that you have.* You need to be prepared to share the gospel any time, any place. You may have only two minutes to share *the reason for the hope that you have* with someone who has no hope.

The Nine Behavioral Skills are communication skills you can learn. The Ninth Behavioral Skill is the Natural Self. The Natural Self is simply being yourself. It is that unique combination of your unique personality, mind, opinions, and behaviors. When we freely express that natural self, we are effective. We communicate with excitement, enthusiasm, and confidence—and reach the First Brain of our listeners, naturally.[1] So, when communicating be authentic, just be yourself. When you share your faith with others, be your natural self. God will use you to affect people.

Review the Nine Behavioral Skills and the Decker Grid System in weeks 1-7. Be prepared to use these tools to effectively share your faith with others. Ask God for opportunities to share your faith.

But in your hearts set apart Christ as Lord. Always be prepared to give an answer to everyone who asks you to give the reason for the hope that you have (1 Pet. 3:15).

DAY 2

The "Telling Your Story" Grid

Consequently, faith comes from hearing the message, and the message is heard through the word of Christ (Rom. 10:17). To be heard, that message must be spoken. Your words may fall on deaf ears, or ears not yet ready to hear. But your words will not come back void as it is promised in Isaiah 55:11, *"So is my word that goes out from my mouth: It will not return to me empty, but will accomplish what I desire and achieve the purpose for which I sent it."* The only loss will be if you never tell others about Jesus. When you speak boldly with confidence about Jesus, it is a win-win: the other person wins, and you win.

"So is my word that goes out from my mouth: It will not return to me empty, but will accomplish what I desire and achieve the purpose for which I sent it" (Isa. 55:11).

When you are telling your story there are three things you want to communicate:

(1) What your life was like before.

(2) What happened when you accepted Christ.

(3) What your life is like now.

The Telling Your Story Cornerstones is a guide (pp. 87-88) to help you share your story. The Point of View is "Christ can change your life. He changed my life." That is the message you want to get across. If you are speaking to an individual or a group of seekers, you will need to know who they are (Listeners). Attempt to know their spiritual temperature. Are your listeners open to the gospel, neutral to the gospel, or hostile to the gospel? Develop a specific Action Step for them to take. Then be prepared to give the Benefits of becoming a Christian. Examples of Action Steps and Benefits are given on the Telling Your Story Cornerstone pages 87-88.

The Telling Your Story Grid is a tool to develop your testimony. Start with the Key Points. First you are going to tell them (1) what your life was like, (2) what happened, and (3) what your life is like now. List two or three ideas under each Key Point, using trigger words. This is a Quick Grid; you can amplify on it later. It will begin framing your mind with what you want to say when sharing your testimony. It is a wonderful experience when you share your faith with others.

Activity: Do the quick exercise in the paragraphs above as you begin the process of putting together your story. Place your Post-its on the Telling Your Story Grid (pp. 87-88).

DAY 3

Developing Your Story

I recommend that followers of Christ be ready, willing, and able to share Jesus Christ with others. That means sharing your transformed life—whether it's in 30 seconds, 2 minutes, 5 minutes, or 20 minutes. Telling others how Christ changed your life can have a powerful impact on those who are without hope.

In Matthew 5:14-16 Jesus says, *"You are the light of the world. A city on a hill cannot be hidden. Neither do people light a lamp and put it under a bowl. Instead they put it on its stand, and it gives light to everyone in the house. In the same way, let your light shine before men, that they may see your good deeds and praise your Father in heaven."* Our purpose in witnessing and sharing our lives with others is being lights to the world.

Some tips for developing your story:

1. Be short with the resume material. Quickly give your background so people have a context of where you've come from.

2. Don't be too graphic if you had a very sinful past. It's enough to refer to it, but you don't want to dwell in it long. Say what has changed, but you don't be too graphic.

3. Spend most of your time on the present. What your listeners really want to know is what has changed. Tell about the blessings in your life since you accepted Christ.

4. Your story will continuously change, particularly with blessings, so keep it up-to-date.

5. Use plain language that people can understand. Be interesting. Some people are too serious because they are telling about a serious life-change. Think of things that will energize and enliven your presentation. Use the SHARP Principles (pp. 67-72) often.

Matthew 9:37-38, *"The harvest is plentiful but the workers are few. Ask the Lord of the harvest, therefore, to send out workers into his harvest field."* Will you be one of the workers who will reap the harvest? I hope so. Jesus always looked for the harvest. After the encounter with the Samaritan woman at the well, Jesus said to the disciples, *"Open your eyes and look at the fields! They are ripe for harvest"* (John 4:35). There was a great harvest that day. John 4:41 tells us: *Because of his words many more became believers.*

List the Benefits (to you and to others) of sharing your faith with others.

DAY 4

Motivation to Tell Your Story

Telling your story is not easy, for your story is an intimate testimony and a witness to one of the most important events of your life. When you share yourself openly with others you make yourself vulnerable, and there is risk in that. But also great reward, as it is the only way we can really express our love for others, and also give hope to others in an often desperate world. We have to share ourselves if we are to love. It's not enough to just be a good communicator, we must express our love into the world by sharing ourselves with others. *If I speak in the tongues of men and of angels, but have not love, I am only a resounding gong or a clanging cymbal* (1 Cor. 13:1).

My Story

Life was apparently going very well for my wife Deborah and I in the first years of our marriage. We had three children and had moved to San Francisco from the East Coast. We had a successful film company that produced political and documentary films, and I had coproduced an Academy Award winning documentary as well as a feature film for 20th Century Fox. Our lives looked fine on the surface, but underneath it was different.

"The harvest is plentiful but the workers are few. Ask the Lord of the harvest, therefore, to send out workers into his harvest field" (Matt. 9:37-38).

"Open your eyes and look at the fields! They are ripe for harvest" (John 4:35).

Because of his words many more became believers (John 4:41).

If I speak in the tongues of men and of angels, but have not love, I am only a resounding gong or a clanging cymbal (1 Cor. 13:1).

There was excessive alcohol, marital infidelity, and tremendous debt—a result of our lack of discipline, over-indulgence and self-centeredness. We struggled, we knew we were broken, but we didn't know how to "fix" our lives. During this time I wrote down specific goals and started trying to fix everything on my own efforts. About this time Deborah came home from a church she had been attending and told me she had accepted Jesus into her life. As she grew spiritually, I saw changes in her; but spiritual matters were irrelevant to me because I was "making it on my own."

One man's comments caused me to think deeper. He said, "Bert, Let me ask you a question." He took a napkin and drew a circle on it. He said, "Let's say all the knowledge of the universe is in that circle, everything there is to know is in that circle. How big a circle would you make in that circle that represented man's knowledge?" I said, "It wouldn't be very big, maybe a dot." He said, "If that is the case, and we agree on that, how big a circle would you make within this dot of your knowledge?" That illustration spoke to me, because I thought I had all of the answers or was going to find the answers. For the first time I thought, *There must be something else going on. Maybe there is a God.* But I continued going my own way, building a company at the expense of my family. Deborah and I separated for several months after that, but I eventually realized that I wanted my family and agreed to marriage counseling. So I met with Bill McGinnis, one of Deborah's Bible study leaders to sort of interview him as a marriage counselor. Instead we talked about Jesus and we talked about God. He read John 3:19, *"Light is come into the world, but men loved darkness instead of light because their deeds were evil"* and I began to weep. I knew I had an evil heart. I realized there was a separation from God that I was trying to fill by self-achievement. I got on my knees and accepted Jesus Christ into my heart as my personal Savior. I wanted to follow Him and my life changed there. I started reading the Bible. We joined a church. But it wasn't all mountain-top experiences. Soon after that Deborah was diagnosed with cancer and fought it for the next 2 1/2 years. She is with the Lord now, but she never lost faith during the struggle. She was an inspiration. Those years were the best years of our marriage because we grew close as our faith in God grew. God was with us on the mountain tops and in the valleys. Over and over we would recite James 1:2-3 and mean it. After Deborah's death it was a difficult time for me as a widower with three children, but I had Christ in my life and my children had Christ in their lives.

Since that difficult time, I have been blessed with many things. One is marriage to Dru Scott, a strong Christian, and the healing of many difficult times in our marriage with a blended family. God heals and gives us hope. My children are married and their spouses are believers, and I have the joy of seeing my grandchildren grow up in Christian homes.

Faith and hope in Jesus makes all the difference in the world. The blessings in my life since I gave my life over to Jesus are too numerous to mention here. My business success would not have happened without Jesus, but it is a bonus to the peace, love, and joy I now have in Christ. My story is about the power of Christ to change a life. Christ

Consider it pure joy, my brothers whenever you face trials of many kinds, because you know that the testing of your faith develops perserverance (Jas. 1:2-3).

can change your life. He did mine. A miracle doesn't happen overnight, it happens when we let Jesus take over. That's what happened in my life; that's what can happen in yours.

Read the verses in the margin. If you do not know without a doubt that Jesus Christ is your Lord and Savior, stop right now and admit your sin to Him. Ask for His forgiveness and for Him to come into your heart as Lord and Savior. Call your pastor or leader of this study and tell them of your decision.

DAY 5

Conclusion

Sharing the gospel with those with no hope is the ultimate purpose of *Communicating with Bold Assurance*. God has entrusted Bold Assurance Ministries to me so that I can share with believers the benefit of my life work. As Christians we have the most important message, the good news of Jesus Christ. My prayer is that you will boldly share Jesus with others. Have a Forward Lean in giving your testimony to those who have no hope. I urge you to make yourself available to God. Ask God to use your story to affect others. Communicate God's love to others with bold assurance, trusting Him for the results.

Communicating with Bold Assurance is a powerful tool to help you communicate effectively. I hope you will use these principles in all of your communications. Now that you are aware of the Nine Behavioral Skills put them into practice. Use the Decker Grid System when you develop presentations and in your daily communications. This will help you develop your ideas quickly and will give clarity to the messages that you prepare. Have a Forward Lean in your communications, be bold. My prayer is that you will use this information to boldly communicate the difference Jesus Christ has made in your life and that He can transform the hearts of those yet to believe. May God use you as you share with Bold Assurance your testimony with others.

Communication Challenge

- *Prepare your "Telling My Story Grid."*
- *Use the outline in the margin to help you share the gospel with others.*
- *I can have a Forward Lean by...*

[1]Bert Decker, *You've Got to Be Believed to Be Heard* (New York: St. Martin's Press, 1992) 271.
[2]Henry Blackaby and Claude King, *Experiencing God: Knowing and Doing the Will of God* (Nashville: LifeWay Press, 1990) 8.

If you sense a need to accept Jesus as your Savior and Lord, now is the time to settle this matter with God. Ask God to speak to you as you read the following Scriptures:

Romans 3:23–
    All have sinned.
Romans 6:23–
    Eternal life is a free
    gift of God
Romans 5:8–
    Because of love, Jesus
    paid the death penalty
    for your sins.
Romans 10:9-10–
    Confess Jesus as Lord
    and believe God raised
    Him from the dead.
Romans 10:13–
    Ask God to save you
    and He will

To place your faith in Jesus and receive His gift of eternal life you must:
- *Recognize that you are a sinner and that you need a saving relationship with Jesus*
- *Confess (agree with God about) your sins.*
- *Repent of your sins (turn from sin to God).*
- *Ask Jesus to save you by His grace.*
- *Turn over the rule in your life to Jesus. Let Him be your Lord.*[2]

CHRISTIAN GROWTH STUDY PLAN

Preparing Christians to Serve

In the Christian Growth Study Plan *Communicating with Bold Assurance,* is a resource for course credit in one of the Leadership and skill development diploma plans. It is also a resource in the Christian Growth category subject area "Discipleship Training." To receive credit in a group study that is 2.5 hours or more, attend the sessions and read the book. To receive credit for individual study, read the book; complete the learning activities; and show your work to your pastor, a staff member, or a church leader.

This page may be duplicated. Send the completed page to: Christian Growth Study Plan
1127 Ninth Avenue North
Nashville, TN 337234-0117
Fax (615) 251-5067
For information about the Christian Growth Study Plan, refer to the current Christian Growth Study Plan Catalog. Your church office may have a copy. If not, request a free copy from the Christian Growth Study Plan office, (615) 251-2525.

Communicating with Bold Assurance
Course Number: LS-0049

PARTICIPANT INFORMATION

Social Security Number (USA ONLY)

Personal CGSP Number*

Date of Birth (MONTH, DAY, YEAR)

Name (First, Middle, Last)

Home Phone

Address (Street, Route, or P.O. Box)

City, State, or Province

Zip/Postal Code

CHURCH INFORMATION

Church Name

Address (Street, Route, or P.O. Box)

City, State, or Province

Zip/Postal Code

CHANGE REQUEST ONLY

☐ Former Name

☐ Former Address

City, State, or Province

Zip/Postal Code

☐ Former Church

City, State, or Province

Zip/Postal Code

Signature of Pastor, Conference Leader, or Other Church Leader

Date

*New participants are requested but not required to give SS# and date of birth. Existing participants, please give CGSP# when using SS# for the first time. Thereafter, only one ID# is required. **Mail to:** Christian Growth Study Plan, 127 Ninth Ave., North, Nashville, TN 37234-0117. Fax: (615)251-5067

Rev. 6-99

We would like to hear from you. If you have completed the *Communicating with Bold Assurance course,* please send us your name, address, and a brief testimony on how this course has helped you to be a better communicator. Thanks!

For information or questions about *Communicating with Bold Assurance* contact Discipleship & Family Leadership Department.

Telephone: 615-251-2833
E-mail: boldassurance@lifeway.com
LifeWay website: www.lifeway.com
Write to us at: LifeWay Christian Resources
127 Ninth Avenue North
Nashville, Tennessee 37234

To find out more about Bold Assurance Ministries visit the website at www.boldassurance.com